The Journey Toward Freedom

Rediscovering the Pleasure of Normal Eating

Kate Butitta, MPH, RD, LD, and Marna M. Canterbury, MS, RD, LD

A Methodist Hospital Eating Disorders Institute Publication

Methodist Hospital

Eating Disorders Institute
Methodist Hospital Eating Disorders Institute
6490 Excelsior Boulevard
Saint Louis Park, MN 55426

http://www.parknicollet.com/edi

The material in this publication is for general information only and is not
intended to provide specific advice or recommendations for any individual.
Always consult your doctor for advice concerning your own situation.

Book design and illustration by J Campbell, ArtVille, Inc.

ISBN: 0-9778900-0-7

First edition: May 2006
09 08 07 06 05 04   1 2 3 4 5 6

This book is dedicated to Baela, Jeffrey and Nicholas,
who show us daily the joy of normal eating,
and to the memory of JoAnn,
who made the world's best meatballs—
and then enjoyed them.

CONTENTS

FOREWORD

N*ormal eating.* What *is* that?
It seems everywhere you look today, messages about food, weight and appearance abound. We are surrounded and bombarded by complex and overwhelming media messages about how we should eat, what we should eat, when we should eat, how much we should eat and how we should feel about it, as well as how we should look, dress, present, fix and change our bodies. These messages can be largely at odds with one another when you compare the messages promoting gigantic, dollar-conscious meals with the messages to be thin or muscular or attractive at any cost.

All of these messages entirely ignore an underlying tenet of normal eating—that is, that we as individuals can recognize and respond to the body's innate hunger cues by eating foods that the body wants and needs to function well, in amounts that satisfy hunger and promote peaceful well-being. Some skeptics believe that left alone to listen and respond to bodily hunger cues, people will be unable to choose a varied, healthful diet and will overconsume foods of one type while completely ignoring other food groups. This viewpoint would support that people need firm guidance about what foods are "good to eat" and what foods are "bad to eat" and should use this information to make decisions about what to consume. This book challenges that skeptical viewpoint and encourages people to truly listen to the cues the body gives them to help guide their food choices. This approach, trusting the body and its wisdom, can indeed result in a healthful, varied, well-balanced diet that will nourish the body and soul. It will take practice, some trial and error, and some time, but this elusive normal eating concept can become the new reality in your life.

Far too many individuals in this world are bound by issues of eating and weight. For those individuals, the word "normal" is often distant and unachievable. Obsessive thinking about food, weight and body image is the ultimate roadblock to achieving the freedom that is so badly needed to be able to proceed with a normal life. Yet finding the balance in practical terms presents a challenge that can be hard to overcome.

This book reviews the subject of normalizing eating in a new light—with a thoughtful approach from individuals who are highly respected for their expertise and experience with these issues. The authors' simplified discussion presents a new perspective and helps makes the seemingly unachievable reality of normal eating possible to anyone with even a little motivation for recovery. The practical examples and real-life experiences give new meaning to full integration of these principles in one's lifestyle and allow for freedom that brings satisfaction and a renewal for life.

It is our sincere wish for you that you will not only find this book to be helpful in overcoming your nutrition and eating issues but that you will use the information to truly find a new way of living. And a life free of eating issues is a better life indeed!

Joel P. Jahraus, MD
Department Chair and Medical Director
Methodist Hospital Eating Disorders Institute

Jillian K. Croll, PhD, RD, MPH, LD
Clinical Practice Director
Research, Education and Outreach
Methodist Hospital Eating Disorders Institute

PREFACE

Before you opened this book, you may have wondered, "Why should I read yet *another* book about nutrition? What makes this book so unique?" Although there are hundreds of books about what to eat or how much to eat, this book is different. *It's about eating normally.*

The Journey Toward Freedom: Rediscovering the Pleasure of Normal Eating is about a different way of eating that really isn't new at all. Unlike the current headlines, this book will not declare a new list of "good foods" or "bad foods." It is certainly not another diet book that just encourages rigid food rules and restrictive eating. Rather, this book will help you sort through nutrition confusion and discover what it means to eat normally.

This book is for anyone who has struggled with food and wants to rediscover the pleasure and freedom of eating "normally"—the freedom to eat according to natural hunger, taste and appetite. This book will help you gain confidence to choose a snack, eat in a restaurant or enjoy a delicious meal with family and friends without worrying about whether your choices adhere to a particular "diet."

The Journey Toward Freedom was written to help you identify misinformation that can keep you feeling afraid of food and obsessing about your body weight or shape. It is based not on the ill-founded notion that food is either an enemy or a friend but on the belief that you can actually eat well and enjoy food. The concepts are based on the science of good nutrition and health—not on a new nutrition fad or product.

Will you benefit from this book? We hope and believe that you will. This book is for you if you:

- *Repeatedly diet, restrict, skip meals or follow lots of rigid rules about food*
- *Feel out of control about food in general—or out of control when you are around certain foods or when you are alone with food*
- *Feel proud that you eat "super healthy" while others are expressing concern about your eating behavior*
- *Experience overeating, bingeing and/or purging*
- *Use excessive exercise, restrictive eating, laxatives, diet pills or other methods to control your body shape and weight*
- *Feel trapped by constant preoccupation with food, weight, nutrition, body size and shape*
- *Feel alone, different and isolated with respect to your relationship with food*
- *Wonder what it would be like to be without these disordered eating and thinking patterns*

We believe that the concepts in this book will help you the way they have helped thousands of clients served by the Eating Disorders Institute at Methodist Hospital.

We hope that as a result of reading this book, you will take steps to challenge the voice that tells you that you can't eat "normally." We hope that with time, you will recognize your body's natural hunger cues and trust your meal plan as you learn to enjoy food again—without compulsion and without guilt. We hope that you read this book with an open mind, an open heart and an expectation that you can embark on a voyage that will lead you to the freedom and pleasure of eating "normally." Although each person's journey takes different twists and turns, you have already taken the first step by picking up this book. We hope the following pages of this book offer solutions to set you free.

We wish you well on the journey.

Kate Butitta, MPH, RD, LD
Marna Canterbury, MS, RD, LD
Methodist Hospital Eating Disorders Institute

In order to fully use the individualized meal planning system described in this book, it is important to work with a registered dietitian who has professional experience with eating disorders and disordered eating. She or he can help you find the right balance of foods that will help you on your way to recovery.

CHAPTER 1:
Journey Toward Normal Eating

I magine for a moment that there were no more "rules" about food, that no specific food or nutrient was "bad." Think about what it would be like to eat foods that satisfy you, foods that you enjoy and make you feel good. Imagine that your body knew how much food it needed, that it could tell you when you needed to eat and when you had enough. Imagine being free of rigid rules about food and feeling free to enjoy cookies or carrots, chicken or cheese, burgers or brownies. Imagine that your body, mind and emotions were at peace with food.

This is what the journey toward the freedom of normal eating is all about.

If you currently struggle with eating, you are not alone. Many people— women, girls, men and boys—do not eat normally. They may diet, restrict, overeat, binge or purge. They may obsess about food and count fat, carbohydrates or calories. They may exercise until they are exhausted or injured. They may eat only limited amounts or types of food or not eat at all. They may spend lots of energy trying to control what they eat and how their bodies look. They may overeat in ways that feel out of control. They may binge and feel somehow comforted. They may feel guilty about eating or overeating, then try to restrict again.

These artificial attempts to control eating and body weight just lead people further away from the truth of "normal" eating—that food is meant to be enjoyed, not restricted or abused.

Each person has the ability to eat normally; it's just a matter of relearning how.

Surrounded by media images of thinness and indulgence, you may feel that everyone is either dieting, overeating, fasting, obsessing about food or worrying continually about his or her weight. Many are caught in the vicious cycle of disordered eating. But many have also set themselves free.

A clear destination

As you begin your journey, it is important to know where you are heading. Normal eating may seem like quite unfamiliar territory, but it is actually a natural, relaxed way to approach food. Eating "normally" means eating according to your body's natural hunger and satiety* cues. It means being flexible with the amount and types of foods you eat. It means eating the foods you like. It means working with your body, instead of against it. Normal eating puts food back in its proper place—as a pleasurable part of your life, instead of the center of your life. Food becomes the fuel for good health instead of the enemy of thinness.

Normal eating is not the "norm"

The principles of normal, natural, pleasurable eating may sound like a foreign language to you, and they may very well be. The reality is that current cultural expectations imply that food is to be either restricted, overeaten, overindulged or feared. When you pick up a magazine or turn on the television, you are not likely to find people talking about eating "normally." More likely, you will be bombarded with this month's surefire way to "control your eating" or "lose 10 pounds in one week." One moment, a before-and-after photo inspires people to buy the latest diet pill. The next moment, advertisements for huge brownie delights and over-sized pasta plates grace pages and programs, promoting overindulgence. The contradictions could not be more pronounced—or more harmful.

*Satiety means physical satisfaction with food or "fullness."
You can learn more about this in Chapter 5.

Silencing the critic

Making changes in the way you approach food involves changing what you think and believe about food, weight and physical activity. If you are struggling with eating, it can feel like there is a critic inside your head saying, "You can't eat that; you'll get fat!" or "That food is BAD," or "I need to get rid of the food I just ate." This "voice" is not helpful on your journey toward freedom; rather, it keeps you trapped where you are. The good news is that you can actually turn down the volume on this critic by choosing for yourself what you want to believe, think and do about your eating. Although it can take some time, countering the critic with more positive messages helps you learn to think differently and then act differently about food. For example, saying to yourself, "I deserve to take care of myself," "I can eat normally and be healthy," or "Eating meals and snacks gives me energy" can help silence the critic and help you take the next step toward enjoying the pleasures of eating.

> *"Now that I know that the critic's voice is not my own, I am thinking my own thoughts again. I feel like one person instead of two."*
>
> —*Taylor, age 16*

Normal eating is not dieting

Normal eating is a natural way of eating that lies between the extremes. It is neither dieting nor gorging, neither deprivation nor stuffing emotions away with food. As shown on the "Continuum of Eating Behaviors" illustration found on page 4, normal eating lies in the center of a spectrum of eating styles and beliefs.

On the far left end of the continuum lies restrictive or restrained eating. Restricting is a temporary state where rigid food rules create guilt and deprivation. The goal of restricting is usually to lose weight or to try to reach a self-imposed or culturally imposed ideal body. The typical results however, are feeling deprived, punished and physically hungry. No one can keep restricting forever; it's just too hard on the body and the mind.

The Continuum of Eating Behaviors

Dieting/Restrictive Eating	Normal/Healthy Eating	Bingeing/Excessive Eating
• **Controlled by:** arbitrary diet guidelines that change frequently	• **Controlled by:** internal hunger regulation	• **Controlled by:** emotions or habits
• **Goals are:** unrealistic weight loss and/or control	• **Goals are:** to fuel the body and enjoy food	• **Goals are:** to cover up feelings
• **Rules are:** rigid	• **Rules are:** flexible guidelines	• **Rules are:** to get rid of food by exercising, purging, or restricting
• **Results in:** physical hunger, deprivation and food obsession	• **Results in:** satisfaction	• **Results in:** shame and guilt
• **Feels:** depriving and punitive	• **Feels:** natural	• **Feels:** out of control
• **Rewards are:** feelings of control	• **Rewards are:** health and freedom from food obsession	• **Rewards are:** pleasure and/or feeling numb
• **Temporary**	• **Long-term**	• **Temporary**

On the other end of the continuum lies excessive eating. Excessive eating is also a temporary state where emotions or a sense of "diet failure" drive an intense sense of being out of control with eating. It can be a way to hide from feelings and feel numb. Instead of acknowledging feelings or emotional discomfort, you may stuff them away with food. Food can become a friend, a solace. This excessive overeating creates shame and often backfires into more overeating or self-punishing behaviors such as restricting, purging or excessively exercising.

Often this black-or-white view of food can seem like the only choice. But unlike these two ends of the spectrum, normal eating lies in the gray zone—between the extremes. Normal eating is a long-term way to eat flexibly and naturally. It means feeling free to eat a satisfying amount of food without guilt, self-loathing or "making up for it" the next day. Pleasure and natural hunger balance each other with the result being long-term stability, well-being and a healthier body and mind. Normalized eating does not backfire into overeating or undereating. It is a healthy place that works with your body rather than against it.

Normal eating is natural

Food is fuel for the body and mind. Food is also one of life's pleasures, and your body has a natural system that helps you enjoy food and regulate how much you eat. This complex system of taste, digestion and appetite regulation can tell you when to eat, what it feels like to be satisfied and how much fuel your body needs. You even have unique taste sensors that help define what you like and don't like to eat. Hundreds of hormones, taste buds, enzymes and sensors work together to help you eat enough food— not too little and not too much. These signals have been there since birth, and when given the opportunity, they can work again today. Eating naturally presents that opportunity.

To eat normally is to eat like a child eats–carefree, but not excessively.

Think about how babies and young children eat. When they're hungry, they know they're hungry. They cry and fuss until someone gives them what their body needs and wants—food. They smile and savor the foods that they like. They experiment slowly and cautiously with new foods. They make a face and spit out foods they don't like. They eat rapidly at first, particularly when they are feeling really hungry. Then they gradually slow down as they become satisfied. They know when they are satisfied and have no interest in finishing that bowl, plate or bottle. Food may quickly become a source of amusement as they throw it on the floor. Their bodies told them that they're satisfied, so they stop eating.

Believe it or not, because we were all children at one point in our lives, we all have the innate ability to eat naturally—without diets, rigid rules or measurements. Even in a world full of diets, jumbo-sized portions, and carbohydrate- or calorie-counting, you can relearn to eat normally while enjoying good health and good taste! It's within each of us somewhere; it's merely a matter of rediscovering it. Letting your body take the lead with how much you eat is part of the journey toward freedom.

5

Contemplating the Continuum

Throughout the past months and years, you may have visited many places along the continuum of eating behaviors. As you continue the journey toward normal eating, reflect on these questions to help understand your own eating patterns and history:

- *Think about your own eating now and in the past. Do you recall a pattern of being on one end of the extreme or the other? Have you ever experienced normal eating, either as a child or an adult? How did it feel?*

- *Do you know anyone who appears to eat normally? Have you seen a child eat an ice cream cone with great pleasure yet sometimes not even finish it? Do you know a person who seems to eat a reasonable balance of foods without guilt or even thinking too much about it?*

- *What triggers have caused distorted thoughts about dieting, restricting or other disordered patterns? A comment from a friend? A bad day at work? Comparing yourself with others?*

Take a moment and reflect on your experiences. This activity can help you understand the futility of restricting and begin to visualize the hope of normalizing your eating.

Normal eating is social

In addition to being a mixture of fuel and pleasure, eating is also a way people connect with each other and celebrate together. In all parts of the world, people gather over meals—very often with specific foods. Cake at birthday parties, Grandma's famous fried chicken, a Passover meal, milk and cookies after school, or Christmas dinner are all important traditions. Other rituals, such as sitting at the same place at the table, giving thanks before a meal or having dinner conversation, are ways that food keeps us connected. Recent studies conducted at Rutgers University and the University of Minnesota, for example, have shown that the simple act of eating a meal together can help children do better in school, talk more with their parents, adjust better to issues of being a teen and even have better overall nutrition.

> *"I don't think about food all the time anymore.*
> *I do things with my friends again.*
> *I have a life outside of food."*
> —Katie, age 29

Food is more than just fuel. It's a positive, relationship-building force in our lives. Eating only "diet food," turning down invitations to share a meal, being afraid to eat in a restaurant or being uncomfortable eating in front of others leads to social isolation, which makes the journey toward freedom with eating even harder. Restoring the social aspect of eating is another part of eating normally.

Normal eating is healthy

Popular food lore says that eating "healthy" means depriving yourself of "bad" foods and consuming only "good" foods. We are told to ignore food preferences and choose foods only according to fat grams or carbs or calories. In reality, consistently ignoring what you want to eat and simply eating what you should eat strips the eating experience of both pleasure

Enlisting the Help of Others

As you embark on this journey, think about whether you want to invite others along to offer support. Having others on your side as you return to eating normally can help keep you going when challenges arise. Because it is not the "norm," however, you may need to be selective in determining who can support you in your efforts.

Comments from others such as "Are you going to eat that?" or "Is that all you are going to eat?" are not going to help you stay on the path that leads to food freedom. Sometimes the most helpful form of support comes from eating meals with family or friends rather than eating alone. Remind family members and friends that you just want to eat together and make pleasant conversation rather than discuss eating issues or be monitored during mealtimes.

On the other hand, you may find that keeping your new journey private is the way to go. It's up to you to decide what makes you feel most comfortable; there is no right or wrong way.

and satisfaction. According to the *Dietary Guidelines for Americans*, enjoying a wide variety of foods in a healthy balance is what creates long-term health and helps protect you from high blood pressure, heart disease, diabetes, cancer and other chronic conditions. Eating according to hunger and satiety cues frees you from the latest diet fad and offers a permanent, natural way to maintain a steady, healthy body weight. Eating naturally is not sacrificing good health. Rather, it is an essential way to enjoy a lifetime of good health.

The journey's first step

The journey toward rediscovering the pleasures of eating takes time, and no two people will take exactly the same path. The journey may take some turns and hit some bumpy trails, but each step will bring its own reward. The first step is to decide that you are ready and willing to make changes in your current eating patterns and your attitudes toward food and weight. Acknowledge that reclaiming normal eating is a lifestyle change, not a diet. Once you have decided that you are ready to take that first step, this book will guide you through the rest of the journey.

What *is* normal eating?

- *Normal eating is going to the table hungry and eating until you are satisfied.*

- *Normal eating is being able to choose food you like and to eat it and truly get enough of it—not just stopping because you think you should.*

- *Normal eating is being able to give some thought to your food selection so you get nutritious food, but not being so wary and restrictive that you miss out on enjoyable food.*

- *Normal eating is sometimes giving yourself permission to eat because you are happy, sad or bored, or just because it feels good.*

- *Normal eating is three meals a day—or four or five—or it can be choosing to munch along the way.*

- *Normal eating is leaving some cookies on the plate because you know you can have some again tomorrow, or eating more now because they taste so wonderful.*

- *Normal eating is overeating at times; feeling stuffed and uncomfortable. And it can be undereating at times and wishing you had more.*

- *Normal eating is trusting your body to make up for your mistakes in eating.*

- *Normal eating takes up some of your time and attention but keeps its place as only one important area of your life.*

- *In short, normal eating is flexible. It varies in response to your hunger, your schedule, your proximity to food and your feelings.*

From Secrets of Feeding a Healthy Family, by Ellyn Satter. Copyright 1999. Reprinted with permission by the author.

Defining Your Destination

Normal eating could be a place that you have never been before, or it may be a place you used to know before disordered eating took over. Realize that no matter where you have been, or where you are now, you can take steps on the path to freedom. Reassure yourself that it is possible to eat naturally, to be at peace with food and your body.

Here are some steps toward rediscovering—or forging—a new path toward normalized eating:

• *Name all the reasons you want to eat normally again. Use this list of reasons to keep you motivated to make changes in your eating attitudes and behaviors.*

• *Make a list of food rules that you have used (e.g., "Fat makes you fat," "Clean your plate," "Dessert is bad"). Where did you learn the rules, and how have they potentially blocked your path to normal eating? Review the various food rules that have kept you trapped. Notice how the rules are arbitrary, how they create fear and discomfort, and how they have changed over the years depending on what diets are popular.*

• *List the diets that you have been on. Did the diets result in permanent weight loss? Did the diets help you eat more "normally"? Remind yourself of everything you have already learned about the futility of disordered eating patterns and dieting. Make a choice to avoid restricting, bingeing, purging and other behaviors that keep you trapped.*

CHAPTER 2:
Working with Your Body

It seems that every week, media reports are describing a "new" approach with advice about what to eat and what not to eat. Have you considered that if any of these external methods for changing how much you eat worked, there wouldn't be a need to introduce a new one each week? The truth is, the human body is smart. It knows when it is getting the right kind or amount of food. The body has a set of natural responses, including physical symptoms and changes in appetite, to regulate eating. Your body actually knows how much food it needs. When it does not get enough food at the right times, it will produce symptoms of hunger, conserve energy and even help you seek out food in order to survive. When it gets too much, the body feels full and decreases the physical desire for food.

Your body is capable of guiding your eating. Normal eating works with your body instead of against it. Normal eating actually helps you feel physically better and more in control of your eating than any "controlled" diet plan can.

What happens when you eat too little

When the body doesn't get enough food or goes too long without eating, it makes many changes to protect itself. Because the body knows how much food it needs, a lack of food forces the body to prioritize the way it will burn energy. The body uses energy for everything it does—helping hair to grow and shine, maintaining a safe and comfortable body temperature, moving through physical activity, keeping alert, and so much more. If you

What is "Purging?"

When the guilt and shame of overeating and bingeing escalates, some people experience purging—that is, they try to "get rid of" what they ate. (Merely thinking that bingeing has occurred can also trigger this process.) They may vomit, exercise excessively or take diet pills or laxatives. None of these behaviors is effective in controlling weight long-term. Rather, purging fuels the cycle and keeps some people hopelessly trapped in the whirlpool. Purging can also be associated with serious health problems, fluid and electrolyte imbalances and esophagus damage. People who purge may become dependent on laxatives and diet pills, which may cause long-term negative effects on the body. The good news is that many people who once purged have been set free of these behaviors by discovering normal eating.

are not getting the nutrition you need, you might find that you are not able to concentrate in school or at work. You may even notice that you have become more irritable or moody. Lightheadedness, fatigue, depressed mood, poor sleep, preoccupation with food, poor concentration and constipation are all common symptoms of not eating as much food as your body needs. The body's metabolic rate also slows down to help conserve energy. Similar to what happens to your house when you turn down the thermostat, the body can feel colder when it is conserving energy. You might notice, for instance, that your fingers and toes are cold more often—or that you feel cold when others are warm.

When you conserve energy, your hair may thin, your nails may become thin and brittle, and your skin may break out. A more complete list of physical, emotional and behavioral effects of disordered eating is found in Activity #4, "Honing in On the Signals," on page 16 at the end of this chapter. These physical symptoms are not just inconveniences; they are important signs that you are not eating enough to maintain the health of your body. Long-term damage to major organs can occur if the body is forced to starve for too long.

"I'm afraid about what this is doing to my body."

—*Susan, age 24*

When signals are ignored

Sending out physical signals is your body's first line of defense. When it needs food, it gives out signals to eat—first quietly, then loudly. When those messages are ignored, small waves of hunger escalate into giant waves that can, in time, lead to overeating or binge eating. Being excessively hungry can make you feel tired, crave sweets, think about food all the time and feel less in control of your eating.

Take a look below at the "The Restrict/Binge/Purge Whirlpool," a diagram that shows the restricting/bingeing/purging cycle. When the body has been deprived, it wants more food. When food is available, deprivation usually backfires into overeating. When people choose to diet or when food is not available—such as during famine—the body's natural response is the same. In other words, it's hard to talk yourself out of overeating when you are hungry. The cycle continues when overeating or binge-eating leads to guilt and shame and further dieting, purging or restricting. Like a whirlpool,

The Restrict/Binge/Purge Whirlpool

the cycle can suck you in and make you feel trapped. This cycle can continue until it is broken by normalized eating.

Breaking the cycle is the next step on the journey toward normal eating. Making a choice to trust your body means that you recognize that restricting, purging and dieting feed a cycle of being out of control with food. Eating meals and snacks every three to four hours takes the edge off hunger and helps end the cycle. Staying calm when you think you may have overeaten or binged—then starting over with eating normally the next day—takes the power out of the cycle and puts you and your body back in charge. It can take some courage to take this first step, but if you pay attention to your physical symptoms, you can find yourself feeling more in control, having more energy and feeling generally more clear-headed. These positive effects can help you stay on the path toward freedom with food.

> *"It's just not worth it…the counting, the guilt, the rebound bingeing. I want to just eat… and then go on living my life."*
> —Jenny, age 28

Encouraging signs

The good news is that when eating becomes more normal and the body gets back in balance, most people feel better—quickly. As you travel the road to recovery, check in to monitor your progress and how you are feeling. Notice differences such as reduced preoccupation with food, less irritability, thicker hair, clearer skin, more energy and better concentration. These improvements can serve as important reminders of how far you have come and help keep you on the path toward more normalized eating.

Pleasant alternatives to overeating

One of the reasons that overeating continues is that it can be relaxing. It can numb your feelings and somehow make you feel better. Because you've made the choice to take this journey, you can choose to find new ways to deal with stress and uncomfortable emotions without using food. Try this:

Make a list of 10 pleasant alternatives to overeating—a list of enjoyable things you can do in 10 minutes or less. You can substitute something from the list when you have the urge to overeat. Choose things you can do quickly instead of things that need a lot of preparation. Listen to your favorite music. Reflect on your most enjoyable memories. Journal, do deep breathing, or call a friend.

Many find it helpful to add the words "Wait 10 minutes" to their list of alternatives. Even if you can't persuade yourself to do any of the pleasant alternatives on your list, simply promise yourself that you will set a timer for 10 minutes before beginning to overeat. Frequently, the urge to overeat will pass after 10 minutes.

Keep your list of pleasant alternatives where it is convenient to you.

Honing in On the Signals

As you travel on this journey, it can be helpful to understand changes that may be taking place in your body. Review the checklist below and check off those symptoms you are experiencing now or those that you may have experienced in the past.

- *Can you see how not eating enough is affecting your body?*
- *Do you recognize the whirlpool of the restrict/binge/purge cycle?*

You may check only one or two symptoms on the list, or you may check off nearly every one. In any case, by doing this activity, you can better understand how disordered eating does affect your body—either in ways you can see or in ways you may not see.

Tuning in to your body can help you notice the positive or negative changes that go along with specific eating patterns.

Checklist of Eating Disorder Symptoms

PHYSICAL symptoms of an eating disorder	I have never experienced	I am experiencing now	I have experienced, but not now
Rapid weight loss	○	○	○
Weight fluctuations	○	○	○
Slow heart rate	○	○	○
Low blood pressure	○	○	○
Sensitivity to cold	○	○	○
Cold hands and feet	○	○	○
Growth of fine body hair (lanugo)	○	○	○
Irregular or absent menstrual periods (women)	○	○	○
Reduced testosterone levels (men)	○	○	○
Frequent sickness	○	○	○

PHYSICAL symptoms (continued)	I have never experienced	I am experiencing now	I have experienced, but not now
Dizziness and light-headedness	○	○	○
Muscular weakness	○	○	○
Hair loss	○	○	○
Dry skin, brittle nails	○	○	○
Fatigue	○	○	○
Difficulty thinking clearly	○	○	○
Swollen glands (chipmunk cheeks)	○	○	○
Burst blood vessels in eyes	○	○	○
Tooth decay and gum disease	○	○	○
Damage to esophagus: sore throat and hoarse voice	○	○	○
Abdominal pain and constipation	○	○	○
Water retention and swelling	○	○	○
Headaches and fatigue	○	○	○
Dehydration	○	○	○
Irregular heart beat	○	○	○

(continued on next page)

BEHAVIORAL symptoms of an eating disorder	I have never experienced	I am experiencing now	I have experienced, but not now
Excessive dieting, food rituals	○	○	○
Eating large amounts of food in a short amount of time	○	○	○
Vomiting; laxative, diuretic, or diet pill abuse; use of syrup of ipecac to "rid" food	○	○	○
Fasting	○	○	○
Compulsive exercising	○	○	○
Insomnia and early morning awakening	○	○	○
Layering of clothing	○	○	○
Frequent weighing	○	○	○
Feeling tense at mealtimes	○	○	○
Eating alone or refusing to eat with others	○	○	○
Withdrawing from others	○	○	○
Trying to be "perfect" (thinnest, smartest, neatest)	○	○	○
Denying symptoms or refusing help	○	○	○
Shoplifting and/or petty stealing for money to buy binge-food	○	○	○
Secretive food hoarding (especially at night)	○	○	○

EMOTIONAL & COGNITIVE symptoms of an eating disorder	I have never experienced	I am experiencing now	I have experienced, but not now
Low self-esteem and self-loathing	○	○	○
Suicidal thoughts	○	○	○
Appearing "together" but really hurting inside	○	○	○
Strong belief that there are "good and bad" foods	○	○	○
Constant feeling of being out of control	○	○	○
Out of touch with one's feelings (e.g. anger, affection, humor)	○	○	○
Intense fear of becoming fat	○	○	○
Depression	○	○	○
Irritability	○	○	○
Fear of inability to stop eating voluntarily (bingeing)	○	○	○
Constant preoccupation with food	○	○	○
Constant thoughts about food, eating, weight and appearance	○	○	○
All/nothing or black/white thinking	○	○	○
Belief that eating will result in weight gain or becoming "fat"	○	○	○
Belief you must eat different than everyone else	○	○	○
Distorted body image	○	○	○

DANGER!
Diet Pills and Other Deceptions

The promises scream out...Just pop a pill and get thin! Just a spoonful of syrup makes the pounds melt away! When you think about it, claims such as these seem really ridiculous. Many products promise quick "results" with little effort, but the results produced can keep you stuck— far away from the freedom of normal eating.

The reason is that beyond the false promise lie many hidden dangers. Most products promoted for weight loss are untested, unregulated and unsafe. From herbs to other "natural" products to over-the-counter diet pills or laxatives, these products all have a dark side. The US Food and Drug Administration (FDA) has less power to regulate dietary and herbal supplements than it does other over-the-counter or prescription medications. This means it is up to the manufacturer of the product to voluntarily ensure the safety, dose and effectiveness of the product.

There are many products on the market—most not proven to be safe and some already proven unsafe. For example, ephedra, a product promoted as a weight-loss aid, was shown to increase the risk of stroke, heart attack and other serious cardiovascular problems. Because of these growing health concerns, the FDA banned the sale of dietary supplements containing ephedra in 2004. But many people took ephedra before it was removed from the market. The chronic use of diet pills, whether from "natural" or chemical sources, can be fatal. The FDA has reports of at least 100 deaths linked to the use of supplements containing ephedra.

The bottom line is that diet pills aren't the solution to weight control or good health. Taking good care of yourself with normal eating and active living can help set you free from the temptations of these products. If you are taking a diet product, herbs or a supplement—even one labeled "all natural"—be sure to show it to your health care provider; she or he can help you determine if the product is safe.

CHAPTER 3:
Navigating with the Meal Plan

The journey toward the freedom and pleasure of normal eating is filled with choices about what to eat and how much to eat. As you relearn how to listen to your body's natural cues for eating, one important guide is your meal plan. Like a compass, a meal plan can point you in the right direction without telling you exactly what to do. Since natural eating is probably an unfamiliar place for you right now, you may need to review your meal plan frequently to make sure that you are headed in the right direction. With time, you can look at it less and start to find your own way.

Beyond a diet

A meal plan is not a diet; rather, it represents a natural balance of food that keeps your body healthy, energized and satisfied. A meal plan gives you guidance on what kinds of foods to eat, as well as when to eat and how much to eat.* Meal plans aren't meant to deprive you of food or routinely give you more or less food than your body needs. Using a meal plan helps your body practice eating normally again. A meal plan provides enough structure to keep you on the path toward freedom, but it's flexible enough to show you how to include any food. Because some food situations may be challenging, unfamiliar and even scary at times, your meal plan can act as your guide while you learn to eat normally again.

*A registered dietitian can provide you with a meal plan that is tailored to meet your nutritional needs.

At first, you will need to look at your meal plan at each meal and snack, but eventually, you will be able to navigate your way without it.

If you are working with a registered dietitian, she or he can help you create an individualized meal plan that fits your history, your lifestyle and your path to freedom with eating. Your dietitian will ask you about your current eating habits, preferences and behaviors, and then give you a meal plan with the amounts, types of food and frequency of eating that is just right for you.

Remember...

The meal plan itself is not a destination on the journey but rather a tool that you will use to get yourself to normal eating. Although you will start with a fairly high amount of structure and record-keeping, gradually you will wean yourself from the meal plan and trust your body to lead the way.

"The meal plan helped me learn a good balance of foods and how to listen to my body. I look at it sometimes, but now I just eat.... Food isn't such a big deal anymore."
—Ellen, age 30

Healing through structure

The first goal of using a meal plan is to add structure to when you eat. The meal plan will help you distribute the food that you need each day into three meals and two or three snacks. This approach helps provide fuel for your body throughout the day and helps prevent you from getting overly hungry. Your meal plan will help you evenly distribute the food you eat throughout the day. Instead of restricting all day (which may lead to overeating in the evening), you will be able to have a reasonable breakfast and lunch. Although it may seem scary to eat more food earlier in the day, remember that distributing food throughout the day helps you experience natural hunger cues and supports a normal eating pattern.

A meal plan also suggests times to eat and times not to eat. If you experience binge-eating or overeating, this structure can help decrease urges to constantly graze or to binge in response to emotional triggers. For those who restrict, a meal plan is a reminder to eat at regular intervals. Either way, the meal plan is the key to setting yourself free.

Balancing what you eat

Your meal plan also shows how food fits into different food groups. Each food group provides you with a different mix of nutrients. The food groups work together to ensure you will get all the nutrition you need and feel satisfied after eating. To function at its best, the body needs six essential nutrients in the proper balance:

- *Fat provides flavor to foods and allows skin, hair, hormones, nerves and tissues to stay healthy.*

- *Carbohydrates give you energy for all the things you do each day.*
- *Protein builds, repairs and maintains body tissue.*
- *Vitamins help your body convert proteins, carbohydrates and fat into energy that the body can use.*
- *Minerals help your body build tissue, regulate heartbeat and maintain the health of existing body tissue.*
- *Water keeps your body hydrated, which helps to keep the body and kidneys healthy.*

Without the right balance of these nutrients, your body cannot be at its best. Restricting calories, limiting certain foods, overeating, purging or following other disordered-eating behaviors can also cause the symptoms discussed in Chapter 2, among them weakness, fatigue, dizziness or feeling sluggish. These behaviors can also decrease your ability to concentrate and decrease your body's ability to fight off sickness or infection. Imbalanced eating also makes it difficult to experience normal hunger and fullness cues.

Various "diets" claim that you must avoid certain foods or nutrients such as fat or carbohydrates, but in reality, feeling your best, reaching a stable and healthy weight, and eating naturally depend on eating a variety and balance of foods and getting enough of each nutrient.

Using food groups as your guide

A meal plan divides food into six main groups in order to simplify and balance your food choices. If you are working with a registered dietitian, she or he will teach you the number of servings for each food group that are just right for you.

Even if you don't have access to professional guidance from a dietitian, a healthy balance of foods from all the food groups is still needed to nourish and satisfy your body. The Normal Eaters' Food Guide Pyramid shows the importance of making a variety of food choices and the key behaviors to help you eat normally again. The shaded stripes on the pyramid represent various types of foods that are needed for good health. The Normal Eaters' Food Guide Pyramid also shows that normal eating

The **Normal Eater's**
Food Guide Pyramid

Eat mindfully.

Eat with others.

Include your favorite foods.

Choose a variety of foods.

Listen to hunger and satiety cues.

Eat at regular intervals.

means focusing on key eating behaviors, such as how and when you eat, instead of just focusing on what you eat.

It is not possible to just "guess" a healthy balance of foods that you need from each food group; some general guidelines about the minimum amount of food from each group can help guide your way. Your meal plan will combine foods from the following food groups: grains, fruits, vegetables, calcium-rich dairy foods, fats, proteins and desserts. As you read through the description of each food group, you will see the minimum number of daily servings recommended for each food group. For example, three milk servings are recommended for good health for all adults, but some people may need more.* A balanced combination of foods from the following food groups can fuel your journey.

*Children, adolescents or adults with diabetes or other health problems must see a registered dietitian for individual guidance about how to use the food groups and a meal plan.

Grains

Grains are the main source of carbohydrates and serve as quick fuel for your body. Contrary to what some fad diets say, carbohydrates are the body's main and preferred source of energy, and they don't make you fat. Whether it's rice, tortillas, flatbread, beans or pasta, in most parts of the world, carbohydrates are the mainstay of the diet. Health authorities, including the American Cancer Society, the American Heart Association and the US Department of Agriculture all agree that grains are an important part of an eating pattern that promotes and protects health. Recently, a large study by the National Heart, Lung and Blood Institute affirmed that women who eat a diet higher in carbohydrates from grains, fruits and vegetables, with a moderate amount of fat, had healthier body weights than those who ate more protein and fat and limited carbohydrates.

Fiber is a type of carbohydrate found in grains. It aids in digestion, helps keep your bowel movements regular, prevents constipation and gives the body protection from illnesses such as colon cancer and heart disease. It also promotes feelings of satisfaction and improves the body's ability to handle glucose.

In addition to carbohydrates, grains provide B vitamins such as thiamin and niacin, which help generate energy and make new cells. These important vitamins are more quickly depleted when the body is undergoing stress. When B vitamins are missing, common symptoms that can occur include a lack of energy, nausea, severe exhaustion, irritability, depression, forgetfulness, muscle pain, impaired ability to fight infection, abnormal heart action and severe skin problems.

Many foods fall into the grain group, including breads, cereal, granola bars, noodles, rice and potatoes. For most adults, six servings of grains per day are the minimum recommended for good health. Many people need more than six grains per day; the amount depends on factors such as current level of physical activity. One serving from the grain group includes one slice of bread, 1 cup of dry cereal, a 1/2 cup of cooked rice or pasta, a granola bar or half of a regular bagel.

The whole truth about whole grains

Grocery stores are full of different kinds of cereals, tortillas, breads, pastas and other grains. You may wonder about foods labeled "whole grain." Are they better than other grains? Should all my grains be whole grains? If a food is considered "whole grain," it means that it is made from all three parts of the grain kernel: the outside covering (bran), the starchy inside (endosperm) and the middle (the germ). Research has shown that choosing whole grains more often is a healthy choice, one that may reduce risk for heart disease, cancer and diabetes. Eating whole-grain bread, cereal, tortillas, oatmeal and crackers are all easy ways to slip in servings of whole grain.

Does that mean that grains made from white flour are bad for you? Absolutely not! Just like with other food groups, choosing a variety of foods within each group is the best way to have natural, healthy eating. The 2004 *Dietary Guidelines for Americans* recommends that about half your grain choices be whole grains, but even one or two servings of whole grains makes a difference. Try some of these easy whole grains in your meal plan:

- *Whole-grain cereal such as toasted oats, raisin bran, shredded wheat or other cereals that say they are made with whole grain*

- *Whole-wheat bread, whole-wheat crackers, popcorn or whole-wheat tortillas*

- *Brown rice or whole-grain pasta*

Fruits and vegetables

Fruits and vegetables are also good sources of carbohydrates and fiber and are packed with many vitamins and minerals that your body needs to stay healthy. Citrus fruits, broccoli, cantaloupe and spinach are good sources of vitamin C, which helps heal wounds and fight infections. Dark-orange fruits and vegetables and dark-green, leafy vegetables are good sources of vitamin A, which is important for maintaining good vision and protecting overall health. Fruits and vegetables also contain powerful natural substances called phytochemicals and antioxidants that can help prevent heart disease and cancer.

Flexibility with Foods

Did you notice that some foods may be listed in more than one food group? Each food group is similar in how much energy it produces and which key nutrients it contains, and some foods meet the nutritional criteria for more than one group. For example, if milk is not your favorite calcium-rich food, one stick of string cheese can count the same as 8 ounces of milk. Three ounces of cheese can also count as a protein choice. Peanut butter counts as a fat when you use 1 tablespoon of peanut butter but counts as 1/2 protein when you have 2 tablespoons. Keep in mind that no foods should get counted twice.

When it comes to taste, fruits and vegetables sometimes have a bad reputation. Maybe you were told to finish your vegetables in order to get dessert, which somehow implies that dessert is always preferable to vegetables. Most people have their favorite (as well as not-so-favorite) fruits and vegetables. In reality, if you actually pause and taste any food that you eat, you may discover new likes and even dislikes. Think about the texture of carrots. When raw, they are crisp and crunchy. When cooked, they are warm and soft. (You may like them raw but not cooked.) Whether it's grilled asparagus, kiwi, grapefruit or green beans, fruits and vegetables can make meals more enjoyable, colorful and nutritionally balanced.

Health and nutrition experts recommend that adults get a total of five to nine fruit and vegetable options per day. A few examples of fruit choices are one medium-sized apple (about the size of a tennis ball), 4 ounces of juice, 1 cup of raw fruit, and 1/2 cup of applesauce.

Calcium-rich dairy foods

Milk contributes many essential nutrients to your meal plan, including protein, calcium, vitamin D, phosphorus, riboflavin (vitamin

B_2) and vitamins B_6 and B_{12}—all of which help build strong bones and teeth and prevent osteoporosis. Acccording to the National Institutes of Health, getting enough calcium-rich foods is also important for maintaining healthy blood pressure levels and even lowering high blood pressure.

It is nearly impossible to obtain enough calcium without including milk and yogurt in your meal plan. Sometimes you may be afraid to "drink calories," thinking that somehow milk won't help you stay satisfied. Milk, however, is high in protein and can keep you feeling satisfied longer than some other beverages.

Health experts recommend that all adults get at least three milk or yogurt servings each day to maintain good health. Calcium-rich dairy foods include 1 cup of milk, 6 to 8 ounces of yogurt or 1 ounce of cheese.

Fats

Fat is an important part of healthy, natural eating and part of every cell in the human body. It helps the body use vitamins A, D, E and K—all of which are essential to the body. Fats help produce hormones and nerves, maintain healthy hair and skin and carry much of the flavor in food. Consider the difference between the taste of vegetables cooked with butter versus without it. With fat, a little goes a long way to make food taste great. Fat also helps you feel satisfied longer and helps your body regain a natural sense of hunger and fullness.

Although fat-free diets were popular for a while, most people found them unsatisfying, flavorless and hard to stick with. Too little fat robs your food of flavor and your body of a critical nutrient.

For most adults at least four servings of fats are recommended to add flavor and satisfaction to daily food choices. Examples of fats are 1 tablespoon of peanut butter, 1 teaspoon of margarine or butter, 1 tablespoon of salad dressing and 1/4 cup of olives. Fats can also be found in dishes with a cream base, such as many pasta salads and soups.

Proteins

Foods containing protein are essential because they supply the body with amino acids, which are the building blocks of muscles, bones, blood cells and nerve tissues. Protein is necessary for growth, resistance to infection and recovery from illness.

Protein foods are also good sources of zinc, iron and vitamins B_6 and B_{12}. These important nutrients are often lacking in the diets of those who struggle with eating.

- *Iron prevents iron-deficiency anemia, a condition that can make you feel tired, short of breath, pale and weak. Meat is a great source of iron because the iron in meat is better absorbed than other types of iron. Other high-iron foods include legumes, such as peas, beans and lentils, as well as dried fruits and iron-fortified cereals.*

- *Zinc is needed for growth, development and wound healing. It is found mainly in animal foods such as eggs, meats, milk and seafood.*

- *Vitamin B_6 helps the body use protein. The nervous and immune systems also need it to function properly.*

- *Vitamin B_{12} helps maintain a healthy nervous system.*

Most adults need two or three servings of protein foods each day. One serving is the same as 3 to 4 ounces of cooked beef, chicken, fish or turkey. A 3-ounce serving is about the size of a deck of cards. Other protein choices include 3/4 cups of shredded cheese and 1 cup of cottage cheese.

Desserts

Desserts are a vital part of your meal plan because they add interest and variety. Desserts are often put on a pedestal or may be considered "bad" or off-limits. Desserts, however, are just another food, providing a combination of fat, protein and carbohydrates.

Eating foods that contain sugar can sometimes be scary when you are struggling against an eating disorder. Sugar is found in desserts, some grains and fruits. Sugar is just a more simple form of carbohydrate than starch, and starch actually breaks down into sugar during digestion. Sugar adds flavor to foods and can easily fit into a balanced meal plan. As with any food, too much sugar is not healthy. Including desserts on a regular basis helps you feel less deprived, serves as a reminder that all foods can fit into your meal plan and adds variety to what you are eating. Avoiding

What Really Happens When We Diet?

Diets come and diets go, but they all have potential pitfalls:

- *Cutting out carbohydrates can cause your body to lose its best source of energy, which can lead you to feel more moody and tired. It can prompt you to eat more foods high in fat and sugar in order to satisfy cravings or "the munchies."*

- *If you choose to follow a low-fat, low-protein diet, you run the risk of iron deficiency, which can leave you feeling tired and fatigued. The energy that you get from low-fat, high-carbohydrate foods does not last long, so you will likely be hungry between meals (and thus may overeat).*

- *Liquid diets usually backfire. In the mid 1990s, researchers at Harvard Medical School found that after three years on a liquid diet, 90 percent of dieters were not able to keep weight off, and 40 percent gained even more weight back.*

- *When you diet, you typically lose muscle along with fat, which lowers your metabolism and makes it easier for your body to store fat with fewer calories.*

- *If you decide to fast, keep in mind that most of the weight lost is water. Your muscle mass decreases, which, again, lowers your metabolism. Fasting can be medically dangerous because it leads to rapid loss of water, sodium and potassium, and can lead to a drastic drop in blood pressure, a condition known as hypotension.*

The point is that dieting does not work in the long run but eating a variety of foods in moderation does.

sweets and desserts will most likely backfire at some point and lead to overeating.

It's normal and healthy to enjoy at least one serving of dessert each day. Dessert includes a slice of cake, 1 cup of ice cream, 1 cup of frozen yogurt, a small (2-inch) brownie or a regular-sized (1 1/2- to 2-ounce) candy bar.

Combination foods

Many foods are actually a mixture of food groups, or combination foods. Pizza contains grain and protein; a casserole contains grain, protein and vegetables; and a chef's salad has both vegetables and protein. It is important to remember that while a food contains multiple food groups mixed together, to your body, it is the same as the separate ingredients. If you think about some of your favorite foods, many may be combination foods because they add taste, interest and variety to your meal planning.

Water

Water is essential for life. It constitutes 60 percent of your body's weight. It is important to drink enough water (6 to 8 cups per day), but it is just as important not to overdo it. Hyponatremia, which is the opposite of dehydration, occurs when the body receives too much water. As a result, the amount of sodium, chloride, potassium and other electrolytes available to your body tissues decreases over time and can interfere with brain, heart and muscle function. In addition, if you drink too much water, you may not recognize actual hunger signals because your stomach may be filled up with water.

What about alcohol and caffeine?

Alcoholic beverages are served to adults in many social situations. Alcoholic beverages do not contain essential nutrients, nor do they fit into any of the food groups. Alcoholic beverages may be included into your meal plan, but you don't have to count them. For most adults, moderate consumption of alcohol presents few problems regarding overall health. Current health recommendations, including the American Heart Association dietary guidelines and the *Dietary Guidelines for Americans,* suggest that women consume no more than one alcoholic beverage per day, and men consume no more than two per day. Avoiding alcohol altogether is a good choice for those who have issues related to alcohol dependency or abuse. Alcohol consumption is illegal for those under the state's legal drinking age (often age 21). Remember, any consumption of alcohol can impair your judgment and your ability to drive, so use caution.

The caffeine found in coffee, tea and soda has a dehydrating effect. Consuming more than 200 milligrams of caffeine per day (2 cups of coffee) has been associated with the development of nervousness, anxiety, irritability, gastrointestinal problems and irregular heartbeat.

Fast Facts on Folic Acid

Folic acid, also called folate, is a B vitamin that everyone needs each day. Like vitamin C, folic acid is water-soluble. Water-soluble vitamins dissolve in water and are not stored in the body in large amounts. Therefore, they must be consumed every day to ensure the body has enough to function properly.

Leafy green vegetables, citrus fruits, peanuts, oatmeal and certain breakfast cereals are all good sources of folic acid. Folic acid may help reduce the risk of having a baby with certain birth defects of the brain and spinal cord. If you are considering pregnancy or you have any chance of becoming pregnant, public health experts recommend that you take a daily supplement of 400 micrograms of folic acid to ensure that you get enough this nutrient.

CHAPTER 4:
Logging Your Progress

Initially, meal plan numbers can feel overwhelming. The number of options from each food group may seem different than what you have allowed yourself to eat or how much you think that you should eat. Sometimes, meal plans seem to list so much food that you may ask, "Can I really eat all that food?" On the other hand, meal plans sometimes appear restrictive and you may wonder, "Will this feel like a diet?"

Remember, the meal plan is designed to help you relearn what an appropriate amount of food really is. You may have years of experience with food rules that tell you that you cannot eat or that you must overeat. That is why it's important to use the meal plan as a critical step on your journey toward freedom. Consider it your most reliable compass—guiding you to abandon permanently the diets, rigid rules and punishing attitudes that you may harbor about food.

Following a meal plan is something that you will work toward, not a diet that you go "on" and "off." It's about progress, not perfection. One important companion to meal planning is record-keeping—logging what you eat on a daily basis as you journey toward eating more normally. Writing down your food intake is an important step because it can help you challenge previous beliefs, silence the voice that says, "You can't eat THAT!" and allow you to see progress. You can start by writing down what you currently eat to identify patterns in your eating. It is usually most helpful to review your food record with your registered dietitian. Together, you can often identify things that you are already doing well and then note some areas needing improvement. You might find that you are already doing a lot of great things—such as eating a variety of grains each day, drinking enough water or having a balanced lunch.

Activity #5

Write It Down

Just writing down what you eat each day—in a notebook, in your planner, even on a piece of paper—can help you find patterns in your eating that you want to change.

- *Do you notice that not having enough food at breakfast makes you feel too hungry later? The meal plan can help you spread out the food you eat so that you can feel your best.*

- *Do you find that you are missing out on some key food groups such as calcium-rich dairy, fruits or vegetables? That's good information. Try making a list of the foods in these groups that you like and work on getting more of those foods. Use the meal plan as a checklist to help remind you to include a balance of all the food groups.*

- *Do you notice that you feel too guilty or ashamed to write down certain foods or amounts of food? Remember, many messages convince us that some foods are bad. The food groups in the meal plan can help you see that all foods can fit into your meal plan. If you have overeaten at times, writing this down can also help to identify times during the day when you might need more support.*

Planning the food you will eat each day is a common way to start using a meal plan. Planning can help provide you with the structure and confidence needed to stick with the meal plan. It can also help you feel more comfortable with the totals on your meal plan once you see them spread out over an entire day.

The stages of record-keeping

There are essentially three different tools for recording what you eat: the Structured Food Records, food checklists and intuitive food records.

a) The Structured Food Records

When you first start keeping track of what you are eating, the Structured Food Records will provide you with lots of guidance and the opportunity to monitor your eating patterns. (The Structured Food Record below was designed by the Methodist Hospital Eating Disorders Institute; another version of it appears in Appendix 1.) These records offer guidance and support to keep you on track with your goals throughout the day.

An example of a completed Structured Food Record

Date: **Tues Oct 12**   Goal for the Day: **Eat more for breakfast**

When/Where	Food/Beverage/Portion	Food Group(s)/Serving
8:15 am	I cup Cheerios w/ I cup milk	I grain/I cal/rich
kitchen	I cup coffee with 1/8 cup milk	1/8 cal/rich
	I cup orange juice	2 fruit
	I slice toast w/ I Tbsp peanut butter	I grain/I protein/I fat

**Continue to list your food intake throughout the day and tally your choices at the end of the day to compare to your food plan goals.

	Grain	Protein	Fruit	Veggie	Calcium-rich	Fat	Dessert
Total Foods for Today	7	3	3	2	4	5	1
Meal Plan Goal for the Day	8	2	4	3	3	4	1

Comments: **It felt good to eat more breakfast. I seemed to have more energy for my day. I even got an extra milk at lunch and dessert tasted good. I did pretty well today.**

The Structured Food Record includes space to record portion sizes, the number of foods in each food group, your goals for the week and questions and other comments. It is important to record this information each day; otherwise, it will become quite challenging remember what you

Variety, Variety, Variety

Your meal plan will include choices from each food group to give your body the balanced nutrition it needs. Since foods within each group are similar in key nutrients, you can mix or match foods within each group. Even if you are choosing foods from each food group, sometimes it can be easy to get into a rut and eat the same foods day after day. (For instance, you may be eating only turkey sandwiches for lunch.) Sticking just with foods that seem "safe" might seem easy, but you are missing out on the variety of colors, flavors and textures found in food. Being able to choose a wide variety of foods is part of normal eating, part of food freedom. For example, deli turkey is a protein, as are meatballs, steak, pork chops, cheese or peanut butter. Always choosing bread as a grain serving means that you miss out on crackers, pitas, pasta and other grains. No food within each group is better or worse than the other, but choosing a wide assortment ensures that you get all the taste, variety and nutrients that are unique to each food.

had a few days ago—even yesterday. Daily record-keeping can also help you plan ahead for the next day.

There are many ways to keep a structured record: For instance, by following the example on page 37 or by using the form in Appendix 1 (page 75). Use whatever approach works best for you.

Regardless of the approach you choose, here's how to use the Structured Food Records:

1. *Write down the date, time and location of the meal or snack.*

2. *List the foods and beverages you've eaten and the amount. For example, if you had cereal, juice and toast for breakfast at 8:00 AM in your kitchen, record the amount of cereal, milk, juice and bread and also what they count for. (Refer to pages 75 to 85 for this information.)*

Once you have written down a meal or snack and recorded what it counts for, you can review what else you need for the day. Add your totals up to this point and see how many foods in each group you have left on your meal plan, then plan for the next meal or snack. Remember to spread out your food options throughout the day as you plan.

3. *Next to the foods section is the comment section. You may want to record thoughts, feelings or circumstances that influenced your eating at that time. For example, if you were feeling stressed about an upcoming meeting, you may notice that you ate more or less than usual.*

4. *As you near the end of the day, review your food records to see what else you should be getting in that day, then plan accordingly. It works best to total up the foods as you go along so that you don't get to the end of the day and find that you have multiple food choices remaining—or none at all.*

Keep in mind, food records are a problem-solving tool, not something to be embarrassed about. They simply provide data for you to review and learn from. When you start using the Structured Food Records, you should keep track on a daily basis. This will help you to identify patterns that are helping you stay on track and patterns that may be getting in your way.

Remember, the meal plan is like a compass that you may consult frequently at first, and food records are a great way to get a "reading" on how you are doing. Food records allow you to see how close you have come to finding your way with the goals of the meal plan. By reviewing your food record, you will be able to identify which food groups you were able to get in each day and which you found more challenging to include. For example, you might notice that at the end of the day, you met your goal for servings of grains but came up short with proteins. Or you may have been out to eat at a restaurant and weren't sure how to count things, so you jotted down some questions. You can now refer to the back of this book to find out how to count that chicken-salad sandwich you had for dinner. Double-check your decision by connecting with your dietitian.

In the beginning, you will be using these records all the time, but once you become more comfortable with a variety of foods, you will need the records less often. With practice, you may be ready to start keeping track every other day instead of daily. Your dietitian can instruct you on the best time to make this change and can offer suggestions on how to record less frequently. Check to see how you do on the days you are not keeping track compared with those days that you are. This practice may seem challenging at first; however, keep in mind that letting go of the structure of the food records is a natural step on the journey.

b) Food checklists

As you get used to writing down what you eat, you may gradually move to using some sort of checklist instead of the Structured Food Records. Food checklists are a less structured way of monitoring your eating patterns. Consider for a moment what it may be like to walk in the wilderness. Once you become more familiar with the area, you come to know where you are going without looking quite so often at your compass. Similarly, with the food checklists, you will gradually become familiar with the territory of normal eating and begin to rely less on them for direction. You can start to practice eating more naturally and more flexibly.

You can make your own food checklists in a notebook or on your computer just by including the names of the different food groups along with open circles to represent one serving from that food group. Remember, because each person's meal plan is different, so, too, will be the number of circles representing each food group.

Here's a sample of what it could look like:

Grains   ooooooo

Fruits   ooo

Vegetables   oo

Proteins   oo

Calcium-rich foods   ooo

Fats   oooo

Desserts   o

Here's how to use it:

1. *Look at your meal plan. Write down the names of each food group and make the appropriate number of circles next to each group. For example, if you have seven grains on your meal plan, make seven circles next to the word "grains."*

2. *As you incorporate different foods into your day, put a hash mark through the appropriate circles of each food group. For example, if you have a hamburger,*

you would check off one circle next to protein and two circles next to grains.

3. *At the end of each day, review your record and identify those groups that are either left with open circles or have extra hash marks.*

If you find that each of the circles contains a hash mark, congratulations! You have followed your meal plan on your own with minimal structure. If you find that you have more hash marks than circles in your daily meal plan, it may indicate that you are being more flexible with your eating—and perhaps some days you are also eating less. This pattern is normal within reason. However, if you are finding that most days you eat more than your meal plan, there may be other factors influencing your eating or your meal plan may need to be adjusted.

Sometimes, after you've moved on to this less structured form of record-keeping, you may feel anxious or worried that you are not doing as well as you should be. This feeling is natural, too. Change can be very difficult, and letting go of structure can be intimidating. Talk to your dietitian about how you feel. As you work to normalize your eating, vacillating between high and low structure is perfectly understandable. In some cases, keeping detailed records for a little longer is the best plan in order to help you continue to move forward.

Activity #6

Finding Flexibility and Variety

Look at your eating patterns. How many different choices within each group did you choose? Are you afraid to try new foods? Remind yourself that you get the most benefit and satisfaction from your meal plan by choosing a wide variety of foods within each food group. Consider trying a few new foods this week and feeling the freedom that comes with variety.

c) Intuitive food records

Continuing on your journey, you will start to recognize that you are referring less and less to your compass. Once you feel comfortable using a food checklist, the next step with your meal plan is often to use more intuitive food records, an even more flexible form of record-keeping that lets you decide the way you keep track of your meal plan. These records can be whatever you make them to be. The goal is to encourage you to venture a little farther out on your own with just the right amount of structure and reassurance to know you are on the right track. The freedom not to write down everything you eat can be like rolling down the windows and feeling the wind in your face.

There are no special forms for this method of record-keeping because you will be able to find one that meets your needs. Here are some ideas to help you develop an intuitive food record that is right for you:

- *Write down just the food that you eat—but not the food groups.*

- *Keep track of hunger and satiety feelings only. (Use the concept of hunger scaling discussed in Chapter 5).*

- *Make an artistic meal plan with pictures to help you keep track of food.*

- *Put stickers on a calendar or in a notebook, reflecting how your eating went that day.*

If you are currently working with a dietitian, keep in mind that she or he will guide you toward the form of record-keeping that is best for you. If you are in a formal program and transitioning between programs, such as from a day program to an outpatient setting, you may be asked to switch to a different form of record-keeping. Always refer to your dietitian when you are considering changing the way you are recording your intake.

To measure or not to measure

When you first start learning about the meal plan, you will notice that servings are often measured as tablespoons, half-cups or cups. These measurements might be a mystery to you if you usually just follow the serving size listed on the side of the box or simply pour foods out of the bag until it looks like enough.

An important step to following the meal plan is to gauge what constitutes a serving size without having to measure. One way to size up servings is to measure things a few times at first, then to use your best judgment, try it on your own and see how close you come. If you are having a bowl of cereal in the morning, measure out a cup of the cereal and pour it into your bowl. Observe where the cereal falls in the bowl before you put the milk in. Does it come halfway up the bowl? Does it just cover the bottom? Depending on the size of the bowl you use, the answer can be different each time. In this case, it might be helpful to use the same size bowl so you can trust your judgment and pour the cereal in without measuring. The ultimate goal is eventually to be able to know the portion sizes well enough without having to measure. Don't worry about being exact with the portions; flexibility and variance is part of natural, healthy eating. The idea is to use your best judgment on the basis of initial measurements and not to be controlled by a measuring cup.

Taking it one day at a time

Once you begin to recognize patterns with your eating, you can start to figure out which ones are helping you reach your goals and which are causing

Keeping Your Compass Close at Hand

Forgetting where you put things can be an unpleasant experience. We've all lost our house keys, the remote to the television, even our car in the parking lot. Physically keeping track of your meal plan and food records can be challenging as well. It might be helpful to keep them in a place where you are certain you can find them again. Putting them in the kitchen, in your purse or bag, in your desk—anywhere you will see them daily—is a good idea. Designate a specific folder or binder for your meal plan and records so that you always know where they are.

Support versus Sabotage

You've made a very important life-changing decision to reclaim the joys and pleasures of food and eating! There will be many opportunities to share your journey with others if you choose to do so. Having the support of friends, loved ones and coworkers can make the journey more enjoyable, especially on challenging days.

While many people will provide genuine support, be cautious of those people and situations that could actually sabotage your progress. Be careful not to find yourself dining with a group of people who are all following the latest fad diet or spending an entire lunch hour talking about how many carbs are in a particular sandwich. Be aware that some people may question you—out of either curiosity or skepticism. They will want to know what foods you had to give up or what nutrients you have to count, and they may even try to persuade you to do things their way. Don't listen! Hang in there.

If you do find yourself in a situation that could potentially hinder your progress, speak up. Let the group know that you are making a lifestyle change and you would love their support. If that doesn't do the trick, you might want to seek out some new lunch buddies. Letting people know that you are taking this seriously might be enough to convince them to respect the path that you are choosing. Even if they don't, remember that it is not their decision. Only you get to pick a healthy path for you.

you to get off track. Because patterns are difficult to change, you may find yourself slipping back into your old ways from time to time, and that is normal. For example, even though you are trying hard to drink milk each day, there will be those days that you just don't feel like it and you may give up trying for a while. There will also be days when you want to skip a meal or give up on the meal plan altogether. These are the times when you should turn to your dietitian for support. She or he can talk you through the tough days and encourage you to push forward. Keep in mind that starting to follow this meal plan is a lifestyle change, not a diet. It is not designed to give you "results" in 10 days like many crash diets. It is a guide to help you rediscover the joys of eating in a healthy and fulfilling way. The rewards of following a meal plan are freedom, normal eating and finding your natural eating patterns.

The feel of the open road

Keeping records is part of reacquainting yourself with natural eating. Records are meant to be a guide and offer support for a period of time, not forever. With time, you will transition away from them entirely. There will come a point when you begin to recognize when your body wants to be fed, how much it needs and when it is satisfied. There will be a day when you are able to enjoy the foods you want without focusing on the calories or fat grams or carbohydrates in the food, and you will focus on taste and textures instead.

Remember...

Sometimes it can be difficult to stick to the meal plan, but you can find motivation to continue by looking at the improvement in your well-being. Refer back to the tables on pages 16 to 19, where you identified physical, emotional and behavioral symptoms you were experiencing. Look for improvements, and celebrate your successes!

These moments of freedom will occur as you relearn how to eat in a healthful way. You may not even realize they are happening. You might ask yourself one day, "When did I stop counting fat grams?" or "When did I begin eating my favorite dessert without feeling guilty?" You will begin to realize you are devoting more time and energy to the things you love and enjoy and spending less time worrying about what you have or have not been eating. It is at this point that the rewards of natural eating become visible on your journey.

CHAPTER 5:
Observing Signs and Signals

The human body is amazing. Your body knows when it is hungry, full or somewhere in between. It even has signals to tell you. But if you have been restricting, bingeing, purging or excessively exercising, you are probably not aware of the signals. You may even think that you are never hungry or always out of control. Eating regular meals and snacks and using your meal plan will help your hunger signals become clearer. With time, you can relearn how to recognize signals for hunger and satiety and trust your body to tell you when it needs to eat and when it's had enough.

Hunger signals can be experienced in many ways. Some feel an empty feeling in their stomach, while others may find themselves thinking a lot about food, feeling tired or getting a headache. Satiety signals can feel like being "done" or full. You may find yourself eating more rapidly when you are hungry and then gradually slowing down as you become satisfied.

Hunger scaling is one way to measure the sensations of hunger and satiety. Think about this scale:

0	1	2	3	4	5	6	7	8	9	10
Famished		Hungry			Neutral		Satisfied			Stuffed

Normal eating means eating when you are hungry (about 2 or 3 on the scale) and then stopping when you are satisfied (about 7 or 8). Waiting to

The Importance of Breakfast

You've probably heard the saying, "Breakfast is the most important meal of the day!" Believe it or not, it's true. Eating breakfast shortly after waking gives your body the fuel it needs to prepare for the day ahead. By morning, your body will have gone about eight to 12 hours without food, and you will be ready to "break the fast" and refuel your energy supply.

Within a few weeks from the time you begin to eat breakfast, you will start to wake up hungrier for a morning meal. Breakfast lights the fire—sparks the metabolism—and helps the body get ready for all its daily tasks, such as studying at school, working, walking and concentrating. Expecting the body to work efficiently without fueling it is like expecting a car to drive without gasoline.

eat until you are at zero on the scale often starts a pattern of swinging wildly between two extremes. Learning to eat when you are hungry and stop when you are satisfied is a way to take care of your body, take charge of your eating and continue on the path toward freedom.

When you are following a meal plan and eating consistently (about every 3 or 4 hours) throughout the day, you are reminding your body what natural eating feels like, and your body will adapt accordingly. Your body will begin to respond to being fed regularly by sending out hunger cues at times when it feels hungry. You may not recognize those hunger cues right away, and that is a normal part of recovery. When your eating is chaotic and unpredictable for a long period of time, your body may stop sending those hunger signals, but that doesn't mean your body isn't hungry. Eating at regular intervals will also help to keep your metabolism working at an appropriate pace. Your body will be getting fuel regularly throughout the day as opposed to all at one once, and it won't be going several hours without any fuel at all.

Getting clear signals

Just like a malfunctioning stoplight, hunger signals can be confusing at times. For example, you may find that you don't feel hungry for breakfast at first and think that it's fine to wait until afternoon to eat. You may feel hungrier in the morning on days that you eat breakfast because your body is giving you the right signals. While you are still relearning your hunger signals, it is important to eat regular meals and snacks to allow your body to heal and give you accurate signs about what it needs.

The type of food that you eat can also affect your hunger and satiety. Some foods, such as high-carbohydrate grains, fruits and dessert, give quick energy and leave the stomach quickly. Other foods, such as proteins, fats and milk, tend to keep you satisfied longer. A healthy balance of carbohydrates, protein and fat at meals and snacks will help you get clear and accurate signals.

Mixed messages

Overeating and bingeing can be triggered by stress, sadness, depression, anger and other strong emotions. But being overly hungry can also lead to overeating. Avoiding excessive hunger, therefore, can help you identify what other triggers may lead to bingeing and purging. A key component of

Activity #7

Listening to Your Body

Practice recognizing your own unique hunger and satiety signals. For a day or two, try to assign a number from the hunger scale to how you are feeling. For example:

- *What hunger scale number would you record right now?*

- *What hunger scale number did you experience before and after dinner tonight?*

- *What signals does your body give you to tell you when you are hungry and full?*

You may start to see some patterns such as waiting too long to eat or eating beyond physical hunger. That information can help you change unhealthy patterns and let your body lead the way.

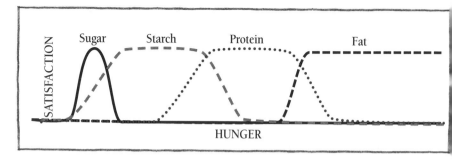

recovery is to identify and learn to manage life's difficult or stressful situations in healthier ways. Working with a psychologist or psychotherapist is an essential part of moving away from unhealthy patterns to more normalized, healthy eating.

Mindful eating

Mindful eating is the opposite of mindless eating—when you eat without smelling, seeing or really tasting it. When you take the time to really experience food, you will likely be more satisfied. Mindful eating is eating with pleasure and without distraction. It is eating what your body is hungry for. It is eating when you are hungry and stopping when satisfied. Here are some keys to more mindful eating:

- *Slow down and really smell and taste the food you eat. You may be surprised about how food really tastes. Find new favorites. Forget tasteless binge foods. Find the foods that please you. Visualize the foods that will satisfy your hunger, focusing on what appeals to your taste buds.*

- *Obtain the food. Get the food that you are hungry for, if possible. Choose a portion that you think will satisfy you after preparation. Choose a serving dish or container that is pleasing to you.*

- *Be more aware that you are eating by turning off the television or radio and even putting away a book. Focus on what you are doing at the moment— eating—rather than distracting yourself from the experience.*

- *Tune into your body by noticing your body's reaction to hunger. Notice the physical signs and symptoms your body gives you.*

- *Begin with the first bite. Take it slowly. Allow the food to remain in your mouth for a while before swallowing. Fully appreciate the taste.*

- *Continue eating. Take several more bites and notice how your stomach feels as it fills up. Become aware of your whole body and your thoughts. If your thoughts stray, try to bring them back to the here and now—your experience with eating.*

- *Finish with full awareness. Be aware of feelings of fullness and satisfaction. Think about the food remaining on your plate; does it still look appealing? If not, allow yourself to become detached from it and clear away the dish. Fully experience the sensation of satisfaction. Compare your feelings now with those feelings before you ate.*

- *Remember to eat before you are overly hungry. Avoid eating beyond feeling full.*

When you drive a car, you should drive without distraction. When you talk on the phone, your best conversations come when you concentrate just on talking and listening. When you eat, the best experience you can have will come through full immersion. Find out how eating really makes you feel. You may be surprised about how enjoyable a healthy portion of food really is.

Activity #8

Responding to Signals

Look at your current eating patterns:

- *Are you feeling hungry but not responding to your hunger cues?*

- *Are you eating beyond physical hunger because you are feeling stressed?*

Start by eating breakfast and moderate amounts of food every three to four hours. Satisfying your physical hunger makes it much easier to resist the urge to eat for emotional reasons.

CHAPTER 6:
Your Natural Body Weight

Do you ever measure your worth on the basis of the numbers on the scale? Do you feel more successful if you look thinner? Do you ever wonder what the right weight is for you?

Measuring your self-worth according to your weight can wear you down, shake your confidence and distract you from what's really important in your life. The media has a narrow definition of what it means for your weight to be satisfactory. In a poll published in *People* magazine in September 2000, 80 percent of women reported that the images of women on television, in movies and in fashion magazines made them feel insecure about their appearance, and 90 percent of women indicated that they had made various and repeated attempts to lose weight to measure up to media images. Women end up feeling so insecure that they are willing to try diets that pose health risks, and they may even go "under the knife" in pursuit of the perfect body.

The media's definitions of a healthy weight are not only unrealistic; they ignore the fact that body weight is just one part of health, one part of who you are. People are different in many ways, weight being just one of them. Height and weight charts are sometimes used to point out an ideal body weight, but how ideal can that weight be if you have to starve to achieve it? An individual's healthy weight actually depends on body build, genetics and natural body shape. If you have petite genes, it's unlikely that you will be the tallest person in the room. If one or both of your parents have (or had) bigger builds, it's likely that your natural build is not going to be thin.

Health at any size

It seems that everywhere you look, someone is talking about the health risks of being overweight. In the meantime, the health risks associated with being underweight often go ignored. Interestingly, years of research have shown that being active and fit, eating well and not smoking are actually the most powerful ways to stay healthy at any size. In other words, weight is not the only measure of overall health, and it is certainly not the best measure.

For example, a person who has a very low body mass index (BMI) might be considered to be at an ideal weight by media standards. But with that low BMI can come a low heart rate and poor concentration. Having an appropriate amount of stored fat is important because it cushions your internal organs from injury and insulates your body to keep its temperature at 98.6 degrees Fahrenheit. People with a low BMI may be missing important nutrients such as calcium, may not be getting a healthy amount of physical activity and may actually have a high risk of some chronic diseases, including cancer.

On the other hand, a person with a higher BMI whose weight might be regarded as above ideal could actually be healthier because she or he may be eating well, getting adequate nutrients and be strong from regular physical activity. Abandon the notion that you can judge your health or someone else's health by looking at weight alone. Making healthy lifestyle choices is the best path to a long and healthy life.

Behavioral mirrors

Another way to view a healthy weight is to look in a different kind of mirror: a behavioral mirror. With a behavioral mirror, you see what you are doing rather than focusing on your physical appearance. For example, if your eating patterns and level of physical activity are healthy and in balance, your healthy body weight will follow. If you are overeating and not being physically active, your weight may be a bit higher. If you are caught in the restrict/binge/purge whirlpool, your weight may fluctuate greatly. If you are excessively exercising and not eating enough, your weight may be artificially low. Healthy bodies come in many shapes and sizes. Health, however, is a product of healthy habits, not movie-star diets.

Why shape matters

Body shapes also vary with family history. Think about how your family members' and your own body are shaped.

Body dissatisfaction develops when you are one shape and want to be another. But it is important to remember that you can only be a bigger or smaller version of your natural shape. If your body shape resembles that of an apple, you cannot transform it into the shape of a pear. It is more probable that your body will either be a smaller or larger apple shape. A person who dislikes her thighs may find that she is not happy with them, even at a very low body weight, because they remain larger in comparison to her upper body.

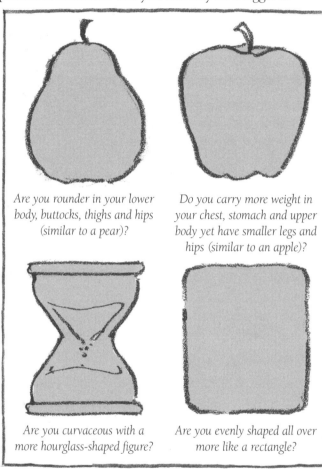

Are you rounder in your lower body, buttocks, thighs and hips (similar to a pear)?

Do you carry more weight in your chest, stomach and upper body yet have smaller legs and hips (similar to an apple)?

Are you curvaceous with a more hourglass-shaped figure?

Are you evenly shaped all over more like a rectangle?

A person may be uncomfortable with fat around the middle but may find that weight loss only leads to feeling thinner everywhere except the middle. Accepting your natural shape and having healthy behaviors can free you from trying to look like or be someone you are not.

What Has It Done for You Lately?

Recognize all the positive aspects of your body.

- *Make a list of the positive things your body does for you each day.*

- *Now focus on a specific body part that you are usually criticizing, such as your thighs, buttocks or abdomen. Your thighs, for instance, can push a stroller up the hill, help you climb stairs, push pedals on a bike and keep you stabilized as you are standing.*

- *Remember that your journey toward freedom will help you take good care of the body you have and keep it healthy and strong.*

Brush-stroked bodies

If you've picked up a fashion magazine lately, you've most likely been bombarded with images of the "ideal female body." There is no shortage of articles focusing on how to lose weight quickly and look like the images on these pages. These articles can make you feel inadequate and dissatisfied, encouraging you to diet. An article may tell you that if you just follow a new diet and exercise routine, you can look like the woman in the magazine—someone, incidentally, you are not. But did you know that many of the women in these magazines are literally unreal? The images we are comparing ourselves with have been changed in many ways.

- *The models' sizes and shapes are altered.*

- *Lines, wrinkles, blemishes and other features are brushed out.*

- *Body doubles are commonly used when the lead actor does not measure up to the "perfect image."*

- *Specific body features are enhanced with lighting, props, camera angles and computer techniques.*

Remember that computer images can be manipulated and regenerated entirely to fit the trend of the day. Between airbrushing and tummy-tucking, the actual women pictured in these photos can be completely recreated.

Sizing Up Your Body Image

Take the following quiz to determine where you stand with your body image. Circle the most appropriate answer for each statement.

1. I want to change a lot of things about my body.

strongly disagree   disagree   agree   strongly agree

2. I spend a lot of time thinking about my body, looking in mirrors, or measuring and weighing myself.

strongly disagree   disagree   agree   strongly agree

3. I feel good or bad about myself as a person on the basis of the number on the scale.

strongly disagree   disagree   agree   strongly agree

4. If I had more willpower, I could be more thin and fit.

strongly disagree   disagree   agree   strongly agree

5. I believe that I would be happier and my life would be better if I just lost 10 pounds.

strongly disagree   disagree   agree   strongly agree

6. I think anyone can look like celebrities if they just work hard enough.

strongly disagree   disagree   agree   strongly agree

7. I sometimes avoid sports or being physically active because I do not feel comfortable wearing workout clothes in public.

strongly disagree   disagree   agree   strongly agree

8. I often compare myself with others and come up short.

strongly disagree   disagree   agree   strongly agree

9. How I look is more important than who I am inside.

strongly disagree   disagree   agree   strongly agree

If you agreed or strongly agreed with four or more of the above statements, you could benefit from a tune-up. Read on for more ideas and tips on how to feel better about your body and about yourself.

Adapted from www.region.peel.on.ca/health/ and www.edreferral.com.

How To Be Your Own Body Guard

1. Listen to your body. Eat when you are hungry.

2. Do self-affirmations daily.

3. Wear comfortable clothes.

4. Cut the size labels out of your clothes.

5. Emphasize your assets. Give yourself credit for positive qualities. If there are some things that you want to change, remember that self-discovery is a life-long process.

6. Make a "Why I Like Myself" list.

7. Take the time to do nice things for your body. Get a massage, manicure or facial. Go get a cup of coffee, read the paper and relax.

8. Set your own standards instead of letting the media set them for you. Question ads. Instead of asking, "What's wrong with me?" ask, "What's wrong with this ad?" Write to the company.

9. Ditch dieting and bail the scale. These are two great ways to develop a healthy attitude and relationship with your body and weight.

10. Accept the fact that your body is changing or has changed with age. In the teenage years, your body is a work in progress. Don't let a new inch or curve throw you off the deep end.

Improving body image means being aware of these images and unmasking them for what they truly are: destructive, superficial and unattainable. These images do not value your uniqueness; they do not honor your wisdom or spirit. They do not measure the person who is you. Your body is miraculous! It performs wonderful feats everyday, puts you in motion, sustains life and accomplishes great things. Your body houses "you" and is certainly not your enemy.

CHAPTER 7:
"But I Can't Eat *That!*"

At this point, you may be thinking that all this talk about normal eating is great in theory but that it would never work for you. You might believe that if you were to eat certain foods—usually "bad" foods—your weight and health would spiral out of control.

Food fears are common. One minute you are told that fat is the enemy and that you should avoid high-fat meats and cheeses. The next day you are warned that eating high-carbohydrate foods ruin your chances of fitting into your clothes. Still other messages claim that certain foods have the power to pull you magnetically toward them against your will, ultimately making you overeat. Statements such as "I could never eat just one cookie" reflect this belief.

The truth is that food does not have any such power. You, on the other hand, do have the power to work with your body's natural hunger instead of against it. You can choose foods that you like and be in control naturally.

The "good," the "bad" and all the foods in between

Many people have certain foods they try to avoid because they consider them to be scary or even triggering. You might decide that putting butter on bread is pointless because the calorie content is too high, even though you really like the way it tastes. Or you avoid vegetables entirely because you think you don't like the way they taste. You may feel pressure to eat

"It's nice to enjoy food again, instead of feeling guilty ALL the time."

—*Gladys, age 59*

certain foods or you may avoid other foods because you are afraid they will affect your body in a negative way. These food beliefs can get in your way as you journey toward more freedom in eating.

Separating foods into good and bad categories is a learned belief. Maybe you were raised in a home where desserts, chips, soda and other goodies were considered "bad," and you were rarely allowed to have them. Diets also advocate a rotating list of foods that are "on" or "off" the plan. If you have a history of bingeing on specific foods, you may start to believe that the food itself is causing the binge. Unfortunately, a strong belief that a food is "bad" results in deprivation and leads you to want the forbidden food even more. This cycle can result in tremendous guilt, and a promise that you will do better tomorrow only fuels the restrict/binge/purge cycle.

In reality, with normal eating, no foods are either good or bad. Food is just food—a mixture of various ingredients and flavors. Including all foods can help you learn to eat normally and according to your natural hunger cues. Relieving yourself of the guilt you feel about eating certain foods can be a powerful experience. Keep in mind that all foods can fit into a balanced meal plan and that deprivation just leads to less control, not more.

Challenging foods

The way you view food and eating can greatly affect the choices you make each day.

Letting go of the notion that you must always control and monitor your food intake is something that takes time, practice and patience. You can start by slowly adding back a few foods that you once placed on your "bad foods" list. Reintroducing or reclaiming challenge foods is part of recovery on the road to normal eating. Trying these foods one at a time can help prove to yourself that they don't make you fat or make you binge. Even a "binge food" can become a possibility when it is reintroduced in safe ways. An ice cream cone with a friend is a safer way to have ice cream than a half-gallon at home alone. One cupcake or single-serving bag of chips packed with lunch is safer than eating out of the bag in the car.

Finding Freedom within the Food Groups

This activity will help you challenge your food beliefs.

• *Make a list of 10 foods you currently think are "bad" and 10 you think are "good."*

• *Using the food lists in the back of this book, locate these foods and compare them with others in the same group. In reality, food is much more "equal" than you may think. For example, white bread, a granola bar, pasta and crackers all fit in the grain group. Peanut butter, chicken and steak are all protein foods. Pizza and a chicken sandwich actually fall under the same food groups.*

Making this comparison can help you realize that foods are neither good nor bad; they just fit into groups and the groups fit into your meal plan. Use this technique when you are worried about eating a specific food or are feeling guilty that you ate it.

CHAPTER 8:
The Trail to Active Living

The word "exercise" may bring to mind images of sweating, embarrassment, competition or pushing yourself to burn more calories. For many people with disordered eating, healthy body movement has also become disordered, either through rigid beliefs about exercise or the fear of moving at all. Physical activity is any kind of movement: dancing, skipping, carrying groceries, hugging, stretching and strolling. Without the negative thoughts, physical activity can feel good.

As with food and eating beliefs, thoughts about physical activity fall on a continuum. On one end of the spectrum lie punishing, lengthy exercising regimes with injuries and fatigue. On the other end is no activity at all—being completely sedentary by sitting, slouching, hiding and not getting out to enjoy life. Good health is actually found between the two extremes, with daily physical activity, stretching and strengthening. The good news is that research has shown—and the US Surgeon General agrees—that daily physical activity for 30 minutes most days has major benefits for health. Walking farther in the parking lot, walking up the stairs instead of taking the elevator, playing a game of tag or vacuuming the living room can benefit the body and cut risks for heart disease, cancer and other health problems. It's really that easy.

The Continuum of Exercise Behaviors

Excessive Exercise	Normal/Healthy Physical Activity	Inactive/ Sedentary
• Focus is on weight loss or "making up" for what was eaten • Rigid rules with guilt • Feels punishing • Repetitive acitivites • Never enough	• Focus is health and enjoyment • Flexibility to fit into the day • Feels fun and empowering • Free to explore new activites • Fun	• Considers moving a "chore" • Loss of confidence in ability to move • Stays stuck • Feels defeating and hopeless • Absence of the joy of physcial movement

A new take on activity

Like developing new eating patterns, considering a new exercise approach involves changing beliefs and taking action. It means reminding yourself that movement in general is good for you and that exercising too much or too little can hinder your recovery. If you find yourself in the middle of the continuum with some kind of daily physical activity most days, congratulate yourself. Focus on the fact that you are active, and resist the urge to tell yourself that your current level is not enough.

Many people find they are at one end of the continuum or the other with their exercise patterns, and they want to find ways to move toward the middle. Yoga, tai chi or other more "gentle" forms of being physically active can help you get in touch with your body, relieve stress and help you feel strong without the calorie-burning mentality. Being aware of daily physical movement can help you discover ways to add steps or to slow down. View housework or yard work as a way to be active. Turn up the music and have some fun!

If you are currently sedentary or are embarrassed to be active in public, you can also add movement by

- *Adding five to 10 minutes of stretching once a day, focusing on how good it feels to move and release stress*

- *Finding ways to add activity each day, such as by parking a little farther away in the parking lot, taking a flight or two of stairs instead of the elevator, or even playing a game of tag*

- *Choosing a more active hobby such as gardening, bowling or bird watching*

If you currently exercise rigidly or excessively or feel guilty when you don't get a daily "workout," try to

- *Change thinking patterns. If you find yourself thinking about how many calories you are burning on the treadmill, focus instead on how good it feels, how strong your body is, the rhythm of the steps, the music you are listening to, the stress that you are leaving behind.*

- *Intentionally take days off exercise and fight the guilt with positive messages such as "My muscles are rebuilding" or "Even Olympic athletes take days off."*

- *Enjoy a leisurely stroll outside—alone or with a support person.*

- *Relax in a bubble bath as a way to nurture your body.*

Physical activity and metabolism

Everyone has their own individual metabolic rate, which is the rate at which our bodies burn energy. Many things we do each day influence our bodies' metabolic rate.

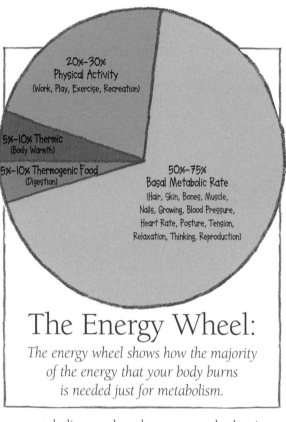

20%-30%
Physical Activity
(Work, Play, Exercise, Recreation)

5%-10% Thermic
(Body Warmth)

5%-10% Thermogenic Food
(Digestion)

50%-75%
Basal Metabolic Rate
(Hair, Skin, Bones, Muscle,
Nails, Growing, Blood Pressure,
Heart Rate, Posture, Tension,
Relaxation, Thinking, Reproduction)

The Energy Wheel:

*The energy wheel shows how the majority
of the energy that your body burns
is needed just for metabolism.*

In order to feel your best, it is important to keep your metabolism running at the rate that is normal for your body. Doing this involves being physically active without overdoing it and eating regular, consistent meals throughout the day. Too much physical activity can alter your metabolic rate, just as too little physical activity can. Because our bodies are built to survive, dieting or exercising to keep your body at a lower weight than normal causes your metabolism to slow down as your body tries to conserve energy. Your body doesn't know the difference between a famine and a diet; therefore, it will start conserving energy and lower your metabolism to survive. Skipping meals, dieting, engaging in extreme physical activity and not being physically active at all can slow your metabolism. As your metabolism slows, you might notice these symptoms:

- *Lack of energy*
- *Difficulty concentrating and solving problems*
- *Headaches*
- *Shakiness/dizziness*
- *Depression/mood swings/irritability*
- *Overeating/craving more intense flavors*

If you are concerned that you may have lowered your metabolism by either dieting, excessively exercising or not getting any physical activity, you can make a few lifestyle changes that can increase your metabolic rate. Start by eating normally and consistently each day; don't skip meals. Then find a form of activity that you enjoy and start moving your body each day. Simple strength training exercises such as exercise bands, handheld weights or certain exercise equipment can build muscles and help boost your metabolism. Be sure to get instructions from a qualified exercise professional, trainer or physical therapist before trying new exercises or equipment.

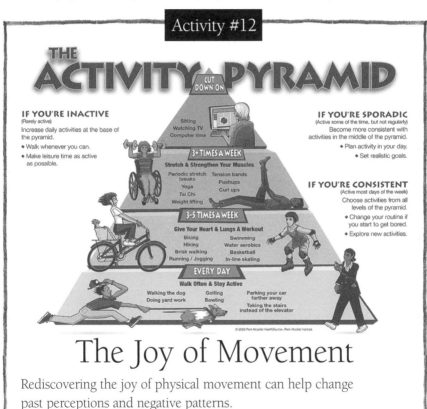

Activity #12

THE ACTIVITY PYRAMID

CUT DOWN ON

IF YOU'RE INACTIVE
(Rarely active)
Increase daily activities at the base of the pyramid.
◆ Walk whenever you can.
◆ Make leisure time as active as possible.

Sitting
Watching TV
Computer time

IF YOU'RE SPORADIC
(Active some of the time, but not regularly)
Become more consistent with activities in the middle of the pyramid.
◆ Plan activity in your day.
◆ Set realistic goals.

3+ TIMES A WEEK
Stretch & Strengthen Your Muscles
Periodic stretch breaks
Yoga
Tai Chi
Weight lifting
Tension bands
Pushups
Curl ups

IF YOU'RE CONSISTENT
(Active most days of the week)
Choose activities from all levels of the pyramid.
◆ Change your routine if you start to get bored.
◆ Explore new activities.

3-5 TIMES A WEEK
Give Your Heart & Lungs A Workout
Biking
Hiking
Brisk walking
Running / Jogging
Swimming
Water aerobics
Basketball
In-line skating

EVERY DAY
Walk Often & Stay Active
Walking the dog
Doing yard work
Golfing
Bowling
Parking your car farther away
Taking the stairs instead of the elevator

© 2003 Park Nicollet HealthSource, Park Nicollet Institute

The Joy of Movement

Rediscovering the joy of physical movement can help change past perceptions and negative patterns.

- *Take 10 minutes to do something fun and physical.*
- *Choose an activity that creates a sense of well-being, such as strolling through a garden, playing hide-and-seek, skipping or dancing.*

Notice how great it feels to be active!

CHAPTER 9:
Staying the Course

As with any journey, while you move along a path to normalized eating, you may wonder, "Am I there yet?" In discovering normal eating, you may have glimmers of change. You may notice that you have had a box of candy for days and not eaten it. You may realize that you relaxed at a meal without counting every bite. You may have enjoyed and really tasted a dessert, yet stopped naturally when you felt satisfied. Each of these moments is a sign of progress, a signal that you are returning to the freedom of eating, listening to your internal hunger cues and enjoying food again. These are indications that, indeed, you are nearing your destination. Not every day will feel that way. Between glimmers of hope may come times when food is overwhelming or scary and feels like it is invading your life again. You may even revisit some of the struggles you faced earlier on your path. This is a normal part of becoming free.

In some ways, the journey toward freedom is not a defined destination. For example, you may feel like you have made progress with food, but physical activity remains negative or nonexistent in your life. You may have mastered the food groups of the meal plan but still struggle with certain foods. You may even feel that normal eating and active living are becoming more automatic, yet you may still struggle with body image. Choosing to focus on your progress instead of what needs "fixing" can help you hang on to new attitudes and behaviors.

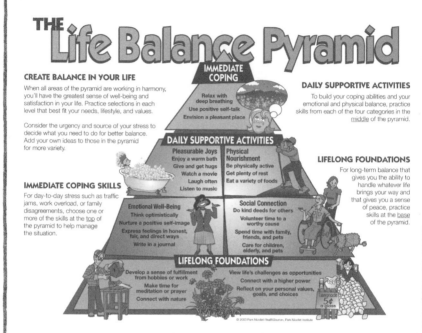

THE Life Balance Pyramid

IMMEDIATE COPING

CREATE BALANCE IN YOUR LIFE

When all areas of the pyramid are working in harmony, you'll have the greatest sense of well-being and satisfaction in your life. Practice selections in each level that best fit your needs, lifestyle, and values.

Consider the urgency and source of your stress to decide what you need to do for better balance. Add your own ideas to those in the pyramid for more variety.

IMMEDIATE COPING SKILLS

For day-to-day stress such as traffic jams, work overload, or family disagreements, choose one or more of the skills at the top of the pyramid to help manage the situation.

Relax with deep breathing
Use positive self-talk
Envision a pleasant place

DAILY SUPPORTIVE ACTIVITIES

To build your coping abilities and your emotional and physical balance, practice skills from each of the four categories in the middle of the pyramid.

DAILY SUPPORTIVE ACTIVITIES

Pleasurable Joys
Enjoy a warm bath
Give and get hugs
Watch a movie
Laugh often
Listen to music

Physical Nourishment
Be physically active
Get plenty of rest
Eat a variety of foods

LIFELONG FOUNDATIONS

For long-term balance that gives you the ability to handle whatever life brings your way and that gives you a sense of peace, practice skills at the base of the pyramid.

Emotional Well-Being
Think optimistically
Nurture a positive self-image
Express feelings in honest, fair, and direct ways
Write in a journal

Social Connection
Do kind deeds for others
Volunteer time to a worthy cause
Spend time with family, friends, and pets
Care for children, elderly, and pets

LIFELONG FOUNDATIONS

Develop a sense of fulfillment from hobbies or work
Make time for meditation or prayer
Connect with nature

View life's challenges as opportunities
Connect with a higher power
Reflect on your personal values, goals, and choices

© 2003 Park Nicollet HealthSource, Park Nicollet Institute

Finding Balance

Part of becoming free is also realizing how your overall life has become more balanced now that food and weight are not consuming so much of your time, energy and emotions. Look at the Life Balance Pyramid above and become familiar with its concepts.

When your eating is normal, you can focus energy and time on relationships, work, spirituality, hobbies, interests, self-care and other important parts of your life. This is part of the freedom of normal eating.

<blockquote>
"I feel like I am out of jail. I feel free!"

—Mars, age 30
</blockquote>

Lapse or relapse?

The path toward normal eating takes some twists and turns, and even when you are feeling "free" most days, there are times that old attitudes, behaviors and feelings about food, weight, bingeing, restricting or purging can return. Times of transition and stress make you particularly vulnerable to these old feelings. Like a storm that blows you off course, certain situations can result in your wandering off or being directed off the path to normal eating. Don't panic! These moments are called lapses. They do not have to become relapses, in which you return to previous behaviors and attitudes that kept you trapped for so long. You've learned a lot on your journey! You may revisit these less pleasurable feelings and situations, but you certainly don't have to stay there.

To get back on track, pick up the tools that you used along the way: your meal plan, your support system, your list of pleasant alternatives to eating, your healthier body image and your

Holiday Helpers

You may recognize situations or other factors that make it hard for you to keep eating normally. Holidays, certain family gatherings, strong emotions, relationship issues, travel or seasonal changes can all affect your eating. As you recognize these situations, you can anticipate and prepare for them instead of just reacting. For example, if certain family gatherings have resulted in your eating spiraling out of control, make sure to eat before you go. You might consider preplanning some of your food choices that day. You can also bring games or activities to help focus the event on something other than just food. If you have a difficult day, forgive yourself and move on, recognizing that normal eating has its ups and downs.

desire to eat normally. Use the tools readily until you feel steadier again. You can also look back on the progress that you have made. Look at the physical symptoms checklist on pages 16 and 17. Remind yourself how it used to be—and note how much progress you have made.

Your send-off to success

If you have ever traveled the world or visited unfamiliar places, you know that a journey never truly ends. With the experience of moving from one territory to another comes self-awareness, revelations about life and a new perspective. The journey toward normal eating is no exception. In reading this book, you have learned how to work with your body's hunger cues, develop and follow a meal plan, log your progress, reintroduce challenging foods into your life and have fun with physical activity. In short, you may clearly be on the path to normal eating again. It's a good reason to celebrate—and to be at peace with your progress.

But with these milestones comes a new pilgrimage, a new adventure. As your preoccupations with food melt away, you may find previously hidden talents and passions. Less encumbered by what and how to eat, you may discover things about yourself that you never had the time or desire to understand. In his poem *The Four Quartets*, T.S. Eliot wrote:

> *We shall not cease from exploration*
> *and the end of all our exploring*
> *will be to arrive where we started*
> *and know the place for the first time.*

It is a wonderful place to be, to realize that a burden has been lifted and that many discoveries—some happy, some sad, some thrilling, some not-so-thrilling—lie ahead. It is the beauty of being alive, to know that we have so much more to experience. Food is just one part of life we are meant to savor and cherish, and it is the reward of the journey that make us rich.

Bon voyage.

Celebrating Your Accomplishments

The freedom of normal eating is a journey, not a destination, but you have come so far down the path. Take a moment to celebrate what you have learned:

- *List ways that your eating, relationships and overall life are better as a result of choosing more normal eating.*

- *Give yourself a pat on the back and reward yourself with something that is special to you—an activity, a balloon or floral bouquet, or even a visit to a special place. Designate a specific time to reflect on where you've been and how far you've come.*

- *If there have been people who supported you on your journey, you may wish to send them a brief note of thanks or include them in your celebration.*

- *Smile when you think about what you have accomplished.*

Always consult a dietitian when working with the Structured Food Record. Feel free to photocopy this record for your personal use.

The Structured Food Record

Date:_____

Food/Beverage	Portion	Food Group(s)						
		Grain	Protein	Fruit	Vegtble	Calcium	Fat	Dessert
	Daily Total							
	Meal Plan Goal							

Comments:

Counting the Foods You Eat

GRAIN Group	Serving Size	Equal to
Angel food cake	1 slice (1¹/₂" piece)	1 grain
Animal crackers, plain, iced or frosted	1 handful or 1 oz.	1 grain
Bagel, grocery store packaged	1 bagel	2 grain
Bagel, from bagel shop with cream cheese	1 bagel	3 grain+ 2 fats
Bagel, from bagel shop	1 bagel	3 grain
Bagel, mini	1 mini-bagel	1 grain
Baked chips	1 handful or 1 oz.	1 grain
Bread	1 slice	1 grain
Bun, hamburger regular size	¹/₂ bun	1 grain
Bun, hamburger very small size	1 bun	1 grain
Bun, hot dog regular size	1 bun	1 grain
Cereals bars (with visible fruit filling)	1 bar	1 grain + 1 fruit
Cereal, dry (e.g., Cheerios,® Kix,® Trix,® Honey Nut Cheerios,® Lucky Charms,® Wheaties®)	1 cup or 1 oz.	1 grain
Cereals, dense, high-fiber (e.g., granola, Grape Nuts®)	¹/₂ cup	1 grain

Cereals, hot	$1/2$ cup or 1 packet, cooked	1 grain
Crackers, regular size (e.g., Ritz,® Triscuit,® Saltines®)	1 handful or 1 oz.	1 grain
Crackers, small (e.g.,Wheat Thins,® cheese crackers)	1 handful or 1 oz.	1 grain
Crackers, very small (e.g., Goldfish,® oyster crackers)	1 handful or 1 oz.	1 grain
Crackers, peanut butter-filled or cheese-filled	15 cracker "sandwiches"	1 grain + 1 fat
English muffins	1 muffin (both halves)	2 grain
Graham crackers	3 squares (1 $1/2$ sheets)	1 grain
Granola bars (hard or chewy)	1 bar	1 grain
Macaroni and cheese, packaged (e.g., Easy Mac®)	1 package	2 grains
Muffin, homemade, small size	1 muffin	1 grain
Muffin, bakery size	1 muffin	2 grains
Muffin, large, packaged	1 muffin	3 grains
Muffin, jumbo (e.g., from restaurant)	1 muffin	4 grains
Pasta (e.g., macaroni, spaghetti)	$1/2$ cup cooked	1 grain
Popcorn, microwave or movie popped	3 cups	1 grain + 1 fat
Potato, baked, medium size	1 potato	1 grain
Potato, mashed	$1/2$ cup	1 grain
Potato chips	1 handful or 1 oz.	1 grain + 1 fat
Pretzels	1 handful or 1 oz.	1 grain
Rice (white or brown)	$1/2$ cup cooked	1 grain
Taco shell, hard	1 shell	1 grain + 1 fat
Toaster pastries (e.g., Pop Tarts®)	1 pastry	1 grain + 1 fruit

Tortillas, flour, fajita or taco size	1 tortilla	1 grain
Tortilla, burrito size	1 tortilla	2 grains
Tortilla, chimichanga size	1 tortilla	3 grains
Tortilla chips	1 handful or 1 oz., about 15 chips	1 grain + 1 fat
Waffle, frozen	1 each (4" square)	1 grain

FRUIT Group	Serving Size	Equal to
Bananas	$^1/_2$ large or 1 small	1 fruit
Fruit cup	1 container	1 fruit
Fruit in gel (e.g., Jello®)	1 container	1 fruit
Fruit juice	$^1/_2$ cup or 4 oz.	1 fruit
Fruit snacks	1 pouch	1 fruit
Fruit, canned	$^1/_2$ cup	1 fruit
Fruit, dried	2 Tbs.	1 fruit
Fruit, fresh	1 cup	1 fruit
Fruit, raw	average piece of fruit	1 fruit
Lemonade	$^1/_2$ cup	1 fruit
Punch	$^1/_2$ cup	1 fruit
Soda	$^1/_2$ cup	1 fruit

VEGETABLE Group	Serving Size	Equal to
Tomato slices & lettuce leaf (when served on sandwich)	3 slices tomato, 1 large lettuce leaf	1 vegetable
Vegetable juice	$^3/_4$ cup	1 vegetable
Vegetables, cooked	$^1/_2$ cup	1 vegetable
Vegetables, raw, leafy	1 cup	1 vegetable

CALCIUM-RICH Group	Serving Size	Equal to
Carnation Instant Breakfast®	1 package	1 milk
Cheese	1 oz.	1 milk
Cheese singles, processed	2 slices	1 milk
Cheese, string	1 oz.	1 milk
Cottage cheese	$3/_4$ cup	1 milk
Milk (1% encouraged)	1 cup or 8 oz.	1 milk
Milk, flavored (e.g, chocolate, strawberry)	1 cup	1 milk + 1 fruit
Smoothie, bottled	8-10 oz. bottle	1 milk + 1 fruit
Yogurt (plain or whipped)	6-8 oz. carton	1 milk
Yogurt, fruit-flavored	6-8 oz. carton	1 milk + 1 fruit

FAT Group	Serving Size	Equal to
Butter, regular stick	1 tsp.	1 fat
Butter, tub	1 Tbs.	1 fat
Cream cheese	1 Tbs.	1 fat
Dips (cream cheese, dressing, mayo-based or caramel dips)	1 Tbs.	1 fat
Gravy	2 Tbs.	1 fat
Guacamole	2 Tbs.	1 fat
Margarine, regular	1 tsp.	1 fat
Margarine, tub	1 Tbs.	1 fat
Mayonnaise	1 Tbs.	1 fat
Miracle Whip®	1 Tbs.	1 fat
Nuts	2 Tbs.	1 fat
Peanut Butter	1 Tbs.	1 fat
Salad dressing	1 Tbs.	1 fat

Sour cream	2 Tbs.	1 fat
Spreads (cream cheese or other cheese-based spreads)	2 Tbs.	1 fat

PROTEIN Group	Serving Size	Equal to
Bacon	3 slices	$1/2$ protein
Beans, cooked	$1/2$ cup	$1/2$ protein
Beef jerky, large	1 piece	$1/2$ protein
Cheese	3 oz.	1 protein
Cheese slices, processed	3 slices	1 protein
Cheese, shredded	$3/4$ cup	1 protein
Cottage cheese	$3/4$ cup	1 protein
Eggs, medium size	3 eggs	1 protein
Fish, cooked	3-4 oz.	1 protein
Hot dog	1	$1/2$ protein
Hummus	$1/2$ cup	$1/2$ protein
Meat, cooked	3-4 oz.	1 protein
Meat, ground, cooked	$3/4$ cup	1 protein
Nuts	1 handful or 1.5 oz.	$1/2$ protein
Peanut butter	2 Tbs.	$1/2$ protein
Poultry	3-4 oz. cooked	1 protein
Seeds	1 handful or 1 $1/2$ oz.	$1 1/2$ protein
Soy vegetable products (soy burger, soy hot dog, soy chicken patty)	1 burger, 1 hot dog or 1 patty	$1/2$ protein
Tofu	$1/2$ cup	$1/2$ protein
Veggie burger	1 patty	$1/2$ protein

DESSERT Group	Serving Size	Equal to
Brownie	2" x 2" piece	1 dessert
Cake, with frosting	$1/8$ of cake or 3" x 3" piece	1 dessert
Candy (e.g., Skittles,® licorice)	1 regular package	1 dessert
Candy bar, regular size	1 bar	1 dessert
Cookies, sandwich	4 cookies	1 dessert
Cookies, homemade, medium or large size	2 medium or 1 large	1 dessert
Cookies, homemade, small size	3 cookies	1 dessert
Danish	1 pastry	1 dessert
Doughnut	1 large	1 dessert
Frozen yogurt	1 cup	1 dessert
Ice cream	$1/2$ cup	1 dessert
Ice cream bar	1 regular	1 dessert
Ice cream cone	1 small	1 dessert
Ice cream dessert (e.g., Blizzard,® Flurry®)	1 small	1 dessert
Ice cream sandwich	1 regular	1 dessert
Malt	1 small	1 dessert
Milkshake	1 small	1 dessert
Pie	$1/8$ of pie	1 dessert
Pudding	1 cup	1 dessert
Sundae	1 small	1 dessert
Sweet roll	1 medium	1 dessert

RESTAURANT Group	Serving Size	Equal to
Asian-style noodles, fried rice dish with meat or tofu, or vegetables and rice	2 cups	2 grains + 1 protein + 1 vegetable + 1 fat
Asian-style stir-fry dish with meat or tofu, vegetables and rice	1 cup rice & 1 cup stir-fry	2 grains + 1 protein + 1 vegetable
Burrito with meat, rice cheese, sour cream or guacamole (e.g., Chipotle®)	$1/2$ large burrito	2 grains + 1 protein + 1 fat
Burrito with meat, cheese beans and sour cream or guacamole (e.g., Don Pablo®)	1 regular burrito	2 grains + 1 protein + 1 fat
Quesadilla with meat, cheese, beans and sour cream or guacamole (e.g., Don Pablo®)	1 regular quesadilla	2 grains + 1 protein + 1 fat
Noodle dishes with beef, chicken or tofu	1 entrée	4 grain + 1 protein
Noodle dishes with beef, chicken or tofu and cream sauce	1 entrée	4 grain + 1 protein + 1 fat
Sub-style sandwich with meat, cheese, dressing and vegetables	6-inch sandwich	2 grains + 1 protein + 1 fat + 1 vegetable

COMBINATION FOODS	Serving Size	Equal to
Casserole with rice or pasta, cream sauce and meat	1 $\frac{1}{2}$ cups	1 protein + 2 grains + 1 fat
Casserole with tomato sauce, noodles or rice and meat	1 $\frac{1}{2}$ cups	1 protein + 1 vegetable + 2 grains
Chili with meat or beans or both	1 cup	1 grain + $\frac{1}{2}$ protein + 1 vegetable
Entrée, frozen, with meat, grain (noodles or rice) and vegetable with a cream sauce or gravy (e.g., Budget Gourmet,® Michelina's®)	1 entrée	1 protein + 1 grain + 1 vegetable + 1 fat
Entrée, frozen, with noodles or rice and meat or fish (e.g., Budget Gourmet,® Michelina's®)	1 entrée	1 protein + 1 grain
Entrée, frozen, with rice or noodles, meat or fish, and cream sauce or gravy (e.g., Budget Gourmet,® Michelina's®)	1 entrée	1 protein + 1 grain + 1 fat
Entrée, frozen, with noodles or rice, meat or fish, and vegetable or tomato-based sauce (e.g., Budget Gourmet,® Michelina's®)	1 entrée	1 protein + 1 grain + 1 vegetable
Hard-shell taco with meat, cheese, lettuce and tomato	1 taco	1 grain + $\frac{1}{2}$ protein + 1 fat
Lasagna	1 cup	1/2 protein + 1 grain + 1 vegetable
Macaroni and cheese, homemade (not from a box) or restaurant	1 $\frac{1}{2}$ cup	2 grains + $\frac{1}{2}$ protein
Pasta salad	$\frac{1}{2}$ cup	1 grain + 1 fat
Pizza, medium size, any kind	2 pieces	2 grains + 1 protein

Potato salad	$1/2$ cup	1 grain + 1 fat
Soft taco with meat, cheese, lettuce and tomato	1 taco	1 grain + $1/2$ protein + $1/2$ vegetable
Soup, broth-based	1 cup	1 grain
Soup, broth-based	1 bowl	2 grains
Soup, cream-based	1 cup	1 grain + 1 fat
Soup, cream-based	1 bowl	2 grains + 2 fats

APPENDIX 3:
Recommended Reading

Doherty, William
The Intentional Family
New York, NY: Avon Books, Inc., 1997

Methodist Hospital Eating Disorders Institute
How Did This Happen? *A Practical Guide to Understanding*
Eating Disorders—for Teachers, Parents and Coaches
Minneapolis, MN: Eating Disorders Institute,
Park Nicollet Health Services, 1999

Methodist Hospital Eating Disorders Institute
Journeys: *True Stories of Hope and Recovery from Those*
Who Have Lived Through an Eating Disorder
Minneapolis, MN: Eating Disorders Institute,
Park Nicollet Health Services, 2004

Satter, Ellyn.
Secrets of Feeding a Healthy Family
Madison, WI: Kelcy Press, 1999

Schaefer, Jenni and Rutledge, Thom
Life Without Ed: *How One Woman Declared Independence*
from her Eating Disorder and How You Can Too
New York, NY: The McGraw-Hill Companies, 2003

Weinstein, Miriam
The Surprising Power of Family Meals:
How Eating Together Makes Us Smarter, Stronger,
Healthier, and Happier
Hanover, NH: Steerforth Press, 2006

ACKNOWLEDGMENTS

This book was developed by
the Eating Disorders Institute at Methodist Hospital, Minneapolis, Minnesota.
Funding support was generously provided by the Park Nicollet Foundation.

This book was written by Marna Canterbury, MS, RD, LD, and Kate Buttita, MPH,
RD, LD, as a way to communicate the nutrition philosophy of all the registered
dietitians in the Eating Disorder Institute who work at a variety of levels of care.

The authors wish to thank Jane Norstrom, MS, the Eating Disorders Institute's
Research Education and Outreach Director, for her encouragement, contributions
and support through the development process. The authors also wish to gratefully
acknowledge the numerous colleagues who significantly contributed to this book
and reviewed this manuscript. They include the following:

Betsy Christopherson, RD, LD, *Inpatient Program*

Jillian Croll, PhD, RD, LD, *Clinical Practice Director, Research Education and Outreach*

Greg Fedio, MPH, RD, LD, *Partial Hospitalization Program*

Katrina Granholm, MPH, RD, LD, *Manager of Intensive Outpatient Program*

Kay Guidarelli, RD, LD, *Manager of Anna Westin House*

Joel Jahrus, MD, *Medical Director*

Julie Mowery, RD, LD, *Outpatient Dietitian and Clinical Practice Director*

Lois Neaton, PT, *Physical Therapist*

Karen Rowehl, MS, RD, LD, *Outpatient Dietitian*

Ann Tarnowski, *Outpatient Program Manager*

We also appreciate the insights from all the other staff at the Eating Disorders
Institute who supported the development of this manuscript.

Finally, we extend our gratitude to Jeanne Mettner, MA, ELS, of Planetary Ink, for her excellent editing and guidance throughout the process; to J Campbell, of Artville, Inc., for creating the cover design, illustrations and layout that made this book come to life; to Lynn Larson, for her timely coordination of printing; and to Lisa Stammer, of Blue Heron Writing & Editing, for her superb proofreading of this manuscript.

ABOUT THE AUTHORS

Kate Buttita, MPH, RD, LD, is a key member of Methodist Hospital Eating Disorders Institute's Research Education and Outreach department. In her work, she develops programs and has given numerous presentations that promote the concepts of normal eating to patients and professionals. Kate lives in Minneapolis, Minnesota, with her husband and her new baby daughter.

Marna M. Canterbury, MS, RD, LD, clinical professional at the Institute, has more than 15 years of experience with eating disorders and nutrition counseling. An engaging speaker and experienced writer, Marna reaches consumers and professionals with key messages about nutrition and health. Marna lives in Stillwater, Minnesota, with her husband and her 11-year-old and 6-year-old sons.

Methodist Hospital

Eating Disorders Institute

Methodist Hospital Eating Disorders Institute provides specialized services for the primary prevention, early intervention and treatment of eating disorders, using a multidisciplinary, team-based approach across a comprehensive continuum of care, including outpatient, intensive outpatient, partial-day hospital, inpatient, and residential care settings.

Methodist Hospital Eating Disorders Institute
6490 Excelsior Boulevard
Saint Louis Park, MN 55426
1-800-862-7412

http://www.parknicollet.com/edi